LOW TEMPERATURE
PHYSICS

FOUR LECTURES

LOW TEMPERATURE PHYSICS

FOUR LECTURES

by

F. E. SIMON   N. KURTI

J. F. ALLEN   K. MENDELSSOHN

NEW YORK

ACADEMIC PRESS INC., PUBLISHERS

LONDON

PERGAMON PRESS LTD

1952

Published in Great Britain by Pergamon Press Ltd
2, 3, & 5 Studio Place, London S.W.1
and in U.S.A. by Academic Press Inc., Publishers
125 East 23rd Street, New York 10, New York
Printed by J. W. Arrowsmith Ltd., Bristol

CONTENTS

FOREWORD

THE FOUR LECTURES printed in this volume constituted a course given at the Royal Institution in the February and March of 1950. The form and contents of the lectures have been substantially retained, but they have been revised here and there to include some of the more recent developments.

We hope that this volume may not only serve as an introduction to the subject for young physicists who intend to specialize in low temperature physics, but also as a general survey of the field for those whose interest in it is less direct.

F.E.S.
N.K.
J.F.A.
K.M.

ACKNOWLEDGEMENTS

The authors and publishers wish to express their thanks to those scientists and authorities who have given permission for the reproduction of copyright material, and particularly to The Royal Society for Fig. 7 in Prof. Simon's paper and Figs. 13, 18 and 19 in Dr. Mendelssohn's paper, taken from their Proceedings; to the Physical Society for Fig. 20 in Dr. Mendelssohn's paper, taken from their Proceedings; to the Editors of *Nature* for Figs. 8 and 9 in Prof. Simon's paper and Fig. 17 in Dr. Mendelssohn's paper; to Messrs. Taylor and Francis Ltd. for Figs. 9 and 11 in Dr. Mendelssohn's paper, taken from the *Phil. Mag.*; and to the *Journ. de Phys.* for Fig. 13 in Dr. Kurti's paper.

LOW TEMPERATURE PROBLEMS,
A GENERAL SURVEY

by F. E. Simon

My aim to-day is to introduce a course of lectures dealing with Low Temperature Physics, which is now one of the most flourishing parts of modern science. In doing so I want to discuss a few of its general features, and to tell you why this region near the absolute zero excites our attention; a region, incidentally, in which man has considerably surpassed Nature herself.

To get the proper perspective, let us first consider the position at the end of the last century. Atoms were still regarded more or less as real 'atoms', indivisible, and without an inner structure. One was mainly concerned with finding out how these atoms were arranged to form molecules and how atoms and molecules were grouped in different states of aggregation without bothering much about the nature of the forces which were responsible. Broadly speaking, a system is only influenced by a change in temperature if the energy differences associated with some possible change in the system are of the same order as its thermal energy; thus at low temperatures any temperature dependent phenomena are connected with small energy differences. Therefore it was thought that by decreasing the temperature still further one would be able to liquefy or solidify yet more gases with lower heats of evaporation or heats of melting, but that nothing unexpected would happen. Although this prospect was certainly important from the experimental point of view, it did not really produce much excitement among scientists. People busy with such activities were regarded much in the same way as someone who wanted to be first at the North Pole or run faster than anyone else. It is difficult now to realize that only a few years before the discovery of x-rays and radioactivity and the advent of quantum and relativity theory, it was still firmly believed that there was nothing essentially new to be found out. Even scientists such as HELMHOLTZ took this view, although there was no dearth of signs that all was not well with classical theory.

The Principles of Obtaining Low Temperatures

In addition there is one other point which explained the relative indifference of scientists towards low temperature research. According to classical theory, absolute zero was not only unattainable but was without much thermodynamic significance. To understand this, let us digress to consider the principles of attaining low temperatures.[1,2] Fig. 1 shows the entropy of a substance as a function of temperature and a second parameter which, to fix our ideas, we will assume to be the volume. I need hardly remind you that entropy changes are measured by summing up the amounts of heat added reversibly to a system divided by the absolute temperature at which they are added, nor that from the statistical point of view the entropy is a measure of the state of disorder. Thus, as we see in the figure, the entropy is greater for a high temperature than a low one and, in general, greater for a big volume than a small one. In order to draw up such a diagram it is necessary to know something about the specific heats. Now one of the pillars of classical physics was the law of the equipartition of energy according to which the degrees of freedom are 'counted only and not weighted'; among other things this implies that the specific heat of a solid is constant down to absolute zero. On this picture

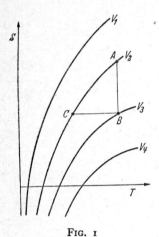

FIG. 1

Entropy of ' classical ' system as a function of temperature and a second parameter V.

the entropy differences between any finite temperature and the absolute zero are infinite, since

$$S_f - S_o = \int_o^T \frac{C}{T} dT = \ln T - \ln 0 = \infty .$$

Therefore in our figure the entropy curves have to tend towards minus infinity as they approach absolute zero.

If we want to lower the temperature, the ideal way is by a reversible process and we can see from our diagram how to carry this out. We start at a finite temperature T_A and begin by changing a parameter (say the volume) from A to B in such a way that the entropy is diminished isothermally. In order to do this we have, of course, to remove a certain amount of heat equal to $T\Delta S$. We then thermally isolate the system and change the volume back to its original value, but this time we do so adiabatically. We now move along an isentropic line and reach the point C, which is at a lower temperature T_c. The total amount of disorder remains constant during the isentropic change; thus, if we increase the part due to the second parameter, that due to temperature must decrease, *i.e.* the temperature falls. This example illustrates the general principles of producing low temperatures: we must have a system at our disposal where the entropy (or the state of disorder) is strongly dependent on temperature and on a second external parameter. The simplest examples of such systems are the gases, and this is the reason why low temperatures and gas liquefaction have for a long time been nearly synonymous.

The Classical Picture

We see at once from the figure that in a classical system it is impossible to reach absolute zero, as all the entropy curves tend towards minus infinity. This unattainability of absolute zero can also be shown in another way. It is easy to derive from the diagram (Fig. 1) that the amount of work needed to cool a substance from the point A to C is $W = H_A - H_C - T_A (S_A - S_C).$ ($H = U + pV =$ enthalpy.) This means that the work needed to cool a 'classical substance' to absolute zero is infinite.

Moreover it is important to realize not only that absolute zero could not be attained but also that it was not a point of great thermodynamic interest. It was not a reference point from which one could count *all* the quantities necessary for thermodynamic calculations, because of this infinite entropy difference.

For all these reasons, seen now perhaps with a certain amount of hindsight, low temperature research had no really wide appeal; few people thought it worth while to start work in this field with all its experimental difficulties when it did not obviously promise results of fundamental interest. Research flourished for a short period in this Institution under DEWAR, and then shifted to Leiden where KAMERLINGH ONNES kept the flag flying practically single-handed.

The Advent of Quantum Theory

The whole outlook was changed by the development of quantum theory and the discovery and interpretation of low temperature quantum effects. Perhaps the most decisive event was EINSTEIN's explanation of the falling off of the specific heats and his prediction that they would approach zero at zero temperature.[3] Entropy differences between absolute zero and finite temperatures were now no longer infinite so that absolute zero could become a thermo-dynamic reference point. EINSTEIN's theory was later adapted to deal with systems possessing a vibrational fre-quency spectrum, and it was shown how to calculate the energy contents of actual crystals[4, 5]. While in general the specific heat curves of real substances vary in a more or less complicated way, theory and experiment both show that they all tend to vanish at absolute zero.

The Third Law of Thermodynamics

Absolute zero became the thermodynamic reference point par excellence when NERNST enunciated the third law of thermodynamics,[6] which he derived intuitively without reference to quantum theory by considering chemical equilibria at ordinary and high temperatures. This law, as we now understand it, implies that the specific heats fall to zero, but it also postulates—and this is more important—that at absolute zero the entropy differences between all states of a system disappear. In a somewhat abbreviated way one can say that all substances at absolute zero are in a state of perfect order—a state of affairs only possible in a quantum world. While the disappearance[8] of the specific heats alone would give rise to an entropy diagram of the form illustrated in Fig. 2a, the third law demands the form shown in Fig. 2b.

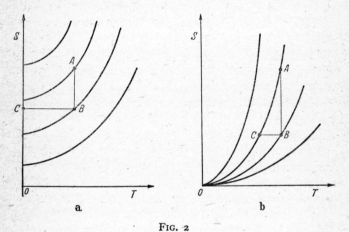

FIG. 2

Entropy of 'quantum' system, assuming (a) non-validity, (b) validity of third law.

Let us now return to the question of the possibility of reaching absolute zero. With disappearing specific heats the work necessary to cool a substance to the absolute zero is now finite and at first sight it looks as if the attainment of absolute zero would be a very easy matter. This would indeed be so, if the only consequence of introducing quantum conditions were to make the specific heats disappear; as we can see in Fig. 2a, an increase of the volume from the point B, say, would lead us directly to absolute zero. The other consequence of the third law, however, is fundamental; all the entropy curves must end up in *one* point at absolute zero (Fig. 2b). We see that, as in classical theory, absolute zero is unattainable, but for quite different reasons and with different consequences; this is a point to which I am going to return later on.

The third law of thermodynamics is to-day the most important guiding principle in low temperature research. At first this law was not generally accepted and obvious discrepancies were pointed out; a super-cooled glass or mixed crystal, for instance, cannot be in a state of perfect order. In fact, experiments carried out on such systems and taken at their face value indicate the presence of entropy differences even at absolute zero. It can, however, be shown that all these systems are not in a state of internal thermodynamic equilibrium, they are 'frozen-in' in a state of disorder characteristic of a higher temperature[7, 9].

Obviously we can only expect to predict the value of the entropy of a system if the system is in a perfectly defined state. For a real system this means that it must be in internal thermodynamic equilibrium, and then the third law of thermodynamics can *always* be applied, as in fact all subsequent experimental evidence has proved. It is important to realize that non-equilibrium systems do not disobey the third law specifically, but rather that the laws of thermodynamics in the ordinary sense cannot be applied to them at all. For instance, it is not possible to speak of the vapour pressure of a glass[7] because its internal configuration and therefore the vapour pressure depends on time—there is no point in trying to apply CLAUSIUS-CLAPEYRON'S equation to it.

After a time of confusion when some authors[10, 11] believed that the third law was sometimes valid and sometimes not, it is now generally accepted as a general law of thermodynamics and is formulated as follows:[12, 13, 14,] 'At absolute zero there are no entropy differences between any states of a system which are in internal equilibrium.' Generally a system is only 'frozen-in' with respect to one parameter and not to all, so the following version may be preferred:[15] 'The contribution to the entropy of a system due to each component which is in internal equilibrium disappears at absolute zero.'

These formulations include of course the law of the unattainability of absolute zero, and it is worth while remembering that if someone thinks he has found a violation of the third law then this would imply—in principle, at least—the possibility of reaching absolute zero. Certainly he would endear himself to all low temperature physicists if he were right, but he would always find, in trying to trace the steps by which he could reach his goal, that the system with which he is concerned is actually 'frozen-in' in some state of disorder: it would be a non-thermodynamic system. The changes in the system which would be needed to reach absolute zero simply cannot be carried out; if, however, it were possible to remove the restraints, which keep the system in a non-thermodynamic state, the entropy difference at absolute zero would disappear.

At first the third law was mainly applied to the prediction of the equilibria of chemical systems at ordinary and high temperatures. This was chiefly due to the fact that NERNST was led to the law by a consideration of just such systems; but there was one other important reason. It was believed that most reaction velocities would become insignificant at low temperatures: changes of the position of the atoms in the lattice, for instance, are possible only if potential barriers can be overcome, and already at liquid air temperatures the thermal energy is small compared with the typical reaction potential barrier. All chemical activities have ceased and the little that was known about the behaviour of solids at low temperatures seemed to indicate that all other atomic processes would die away too. It is true that there were a few exceptions; the electrical resistance of metals was one of them, but even here some people believed that finally they all would become infinite. Searching for this KAMERLINGH ONNES discovered the phenomenon of superconductivity!

Zero-Point Energy

Later on many cases were found of systems in which a great deal happens at low temperatures and these are the ones on which low temperature physics now concentrates its attention. In classical theory the motions of all the particles die out as absolute zero is approached; in quantum mechanics, however, the position is different. A zero-point energy was first introduced tentatively in PLANCK'S second hypothesis;[16] he assumed that the energy of an oscillator in its lowest state was $1/2$ hν ($\nu =$ the frequency of the oscillator). It was then shown that this zero-point energy must produce a difference in the vapour pressures of isotopes;[17] although the available experimental evidence gave some support it was not conclusive. Further indications of the existence of this zero-point energy were given by the study of the melting point and of the law of corresponding states.[18] The first quantitative proof came from the study of the intensities of x-ray diffraction patterns at low temperatures[19] and later the study of the spectra of diatomic molecules[20] gave further confirmation. Finally, the new quantum mechanics showed the necessity of a zero-point energy, and to-day many experimental proofs exist for it.

Perhaps the simplest way to show the necessity of zero-point energy is by way of the Uncertainty Principle. If we try to determine the position of an atom very accurately, the uncertainty of its momentum increases. If one tries to fix an atom in one place by lattice forces then the atom will vibrate even at absolute zero, and the stronger the forces with which one tries to confine it (and the lower its mass) the higher the frequency of vibration and therefore the zero-point energy. A rigorous treatment of this problem leads to just the same expression for zero-point vibration as PLANCK guessed many years before; it may also be shown that other forms of motion, such as rotation, have their zero-point energy. We should note that at high temperatures (i.e. at temperatures for which kT is big compared with the energy quantum) the sum of thermal energy plus zero-point energy approaches the classical value of the energy as indicated in Fig. 3 a and b. At low temperatures, however, the total energy exceeds that of the classical system.

Zero-point energy must affect all properties of a condensed phase, but obviously only to any considerable extent at temperatures for which kT is small in comparison to $h\nu$. Its presence will be the more important the greater $h\nu$ is in comparison with, say, the lattice energy. Thus we would not expect zero-point energy to make much difference to the properties of substances at room temperature, but its effects could become very pronounced in substances with a low boiling point. This is especially true as low-boiling substances happen to possess low atomic weights (and therefore relatively higher frequencies of oscillation).

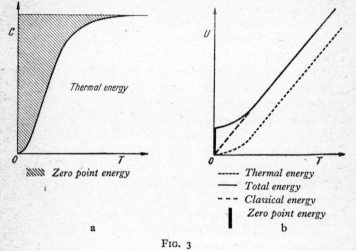

FIG. 3

Zero point energy, Thermal energy and Total energy of crystalline substance.

We find, for instance, that while the total cohesive lattice energy of solid hydrogen is of the order of 400 cal/mole, the zero-point energy counteracts about 200 cal/mole so that the measured heat of sublimation is only 400 — 200 = 200 cal/mole. It is also worth noting that the whole of its thermal energy at the melting point amounts to only 5 cal/mole. Thus zero-point energy must play a determining role in the properties of this substance.

Liquid Helium

The most spectacular effects, however, are seen in condensed helium where about 80 per cent. of the total 'lattice' energy is counterbalanced by the zero-point energy. For the helium isotope with the mass 3 this figure is 95 per cent., which means that it comes very near to not condensing at all (although by exerting sufficient pressure any system could be brought into the state of a *crystalline order*).

The zero-point energy of a substance is decreased if its volume is increased, as this lowers the frequencies of the vibrations. In order to reduce its energy to a minimum, liquid helium has increased its volume (and hence reduced its zero-point energy), to such an extent that it is about three times as great as would be expected from the gas-kinetic diameter of the molecule. Helium cannot solidify under its own vapour pressure and it is therefore prevented from reaching the state of perfect order in the normal way. It loses its entropy by passing into a state of 'liquid degeneracy', (He II), by way of a second order transition, the 'λ-phenomenon'. This liquid degeneracy—related to the gas degeneracy to be discussed later—is the reason for the remarkable effects which low temperature physicists now regard with such interest. Helium below the λ-point—and superconductors—are the only systems in which quantum effects manifest themselves on a macroscopic scale, at least under terrestrial conditions. Professor ALLEN will deal with these effects in a later lecture, and also say something about recent experiments made using ^{3}He which not only exhibits a much higher zero-point energy but also follows a different statistics.

Electrons in Metals

Zero-point energy is also of fundamental importance when we come to deal with the properties of electrons in metals. In pre-quantum times a great number of these properties had been explained successfully by the assumption of a free electron 'gas', but this involved two major difficulties. Firstly, the specific heat of a metal should have included a contribution from the electron gas of $\frac{3}{2}R$, while the measured values gave no sign of this additional contribution. Then in order to explain the values of the electrical and thermal conductivity, one had to assume that the electrons had a random velocity which was constant and independent of temperature.

At first, quantum theory was only applied to vibrations and rotations and not to the translational motion of the atoms of a gas. NERNST, when he first put forward his theorem, only postulated it for condensed phases, but he soon extended it to include gases, not because of any particular theory, but because he felt that if his theorem were a general law of Nature, it should include all phases. He therefore postulated that a state of 'gas degeneracy'[21, 6] should set in at low temperatures and high densities.

The development of quantum theory finally led to a confirmation of NERNST's inspired guess and gave the quantum statistical explanation for it. It was shown that the specific heat of an ideal gas would have to approach zero with falling temperature and that there should be deviations from the ideal gas law given by the two following equations:

$$pV/RT = 1 - \cdot0318A \quad \text{(BOSE-EINSTEIN)} \quad \text{or}$$
$$pV/RT = 1 + \cdot176A \quad \text{(FERMI-DIRAC)}$$

The first formula is for a gas which follows BOSE–EINSTEIN statistics, the second for one following FERMI–DIRAC statistics corresponding to symmetry or anti-symmetry of the wave functions. (A) represents the degeneracy parameter:

$$A = \frac{Nh^3}{V(2\pi mkT)^{\frac{3}{2}}}$$

N = AVOGADRO's number,
h = PLANCK's constant,
k = BOLTZMANN's constant,
m = mass of particle.

Thus the lower the temperature and the smaller the molar volume and the mass of the particles, the greater the deviations from the ideal gas law. These results could not be verified experimentally with ordinary gases, because at temperatures and volumes where the deviations would be measurable the gases would have condensed. Also there is no hope of detecting the degeneracy of a gas just by trying to reduce the temperature, even to the new region below $1°$; the effect of the falling vapour pressure (and hence an increasing molar volume) much outweighs that of the falling temperature. For instance, in saturated helium at $4 \cdot 2°$ the deviations would be 4×10^{-3}; at $2°$, 6×10^{-4}; at $1°$, 10^{-5}, and at $0 \cdot 5°$, 10^{-9}. The value at $4 \cdot 2°$ should still be observable but is completely overshadowed by the much bigger deviations due to the non-ideality of the gas.

When we consider the behaviour of electrons in metals the position is quite different. Owing to the particular structure of a metal we have a very high density of electrons and in addition the mass of the electron is very small. This combination has the effect that the electron gas begins to become degenerate at very high temperatures, of the order of $10,000°$ (Fig. 4). Thus at room temperature, for instance, the electron gas is practically completely degenerate and no considerable contribution to the specific heat can be expected. The detailed calculation shows that finally the specific heat of the electron gas, obeying the FERMI-DIRAC statistics,

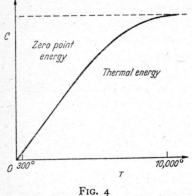

FIG. 4
Sketch of specific heat of the electron gas in a metal.

falls towards zero proportionally to the absolute temperature. This has been confirmed by experiments at very low temperatures, where the specific heat of the metal lattice has virtually disappeared and it is thus possible to detect the extremely small contribution of the electrons. The high degeneracy temperature also implies that the electrons have a very big zero-point energy and this explains why they have a constant random velocity.

Electrical Conductivity

The most interesting branch of electron metal-physics is that of the 'transport phenomena', particularly electrical conductivity. On classical theory it is certainly to be expected that the resistance of a metal should fall with reduction of temperature, since the atoms vibrate less strongly in the lattice, but it was the advent of quantum theory which made it possible to understand the remarkable increase of conductivity at low temperatures. The theory shows that a mathematically perfect metal crystal should have no electrical resistance at absolute zero, though the presence of impurities and lattice defects in real metals seems to keep their resistances finite. It is generally found that the resistance tends to a limiting value which may be as little as 1 part in 10^4 of the room-temperature resistance.

There is, however, one very remarkable exception to this general rule, the phenomenon of superconductivity, which was first observed by KAMERLINGH ONNES in 1911. In certain metals and compounds the resistance falls abruptly to zero at a finite temperature; there is as yet no full explanation of this effect. It is true that the phenomenological theory of the LONDONS[22] has led to a great clarification of the position, but of course not to an explanation of the underlying mechanism. In the last year, however, the theories of FROHLICH and BARDEEN seem to have given the first pointers towards an understanding. Dr. MENDELSSOHN is going to deal in his lecture with this remarkable phenomenon.

Apart from superconductivity there are several other phenomena of great interest, for example the influence of a magnetic field on electrical (as well as on thermal) resistance. I would also like to mention the recently discovered fact that in some substances the electrical resistance shows a minimum and begins to rise again at the lowest temperatures. This is very puzzling and no explanation has yet been given.

Magnetic Phenomena

A third subject of great interest to low temperature physicists will be among the subjects discussed in Dr. KURTI's lecture; it is the study of paramagnetism at very low temperatures, which among other things has led to a very considerable extension of the temperature range available to the experimentalist. Paramagnetism has been known for a very long time to be due to the existence of small elementary magnets. LANGEVIN was able to explain a great many paramagnetic phenomena by assuming that the elementary dipoles were free to take up positions in all directions, as for instance in a gas, and he could give the explanation of CURIE's law according to which the paramagnetic susceptibility varies as $1/T$.

It was assumed that at low temperatures these elementary magnets would no longer be free to turn in the crystal lattice and CURIE's law would no longer apply. Experiments at Leiden, however, showed that for a whole class of substances, in which the dipoles were very far apart, this law held right down to $1°$ K and this could only be because the dipoles had not yet settled into their preferred directions.

Such substances must have a significant contribution to their entropy from the disorder of the elementary magnets and, as GIAUQUE and DEBYE first suggested, this fact can be used to lower the temperature.[23] Fig. 5a shows a simplified entropy diagram of a paramagnetic salt as a function of temperature and magnetic field, and we see that in zero field the entropy is still very high even at $1°$. If the entropy were to remain as large as this down to absolute zero, the system would be in contradiction to the third law and absolute zero could be reached. As this is impossible interaction forces between dipoles and lattice or between dipoles and dipoles must finally remove the disorder—and we know now that there are salts where this only happens in the region of about $1/100°$ K. Hence temperatures as low as this can be reached by a procedure similar to that discussed at the beginning of the lecture, namely an isothermal magnetization of the working substance (A to B) followed by an adiabatic demagnetization (B to C). Fig. 5b shows the specific heat of a paramagnetic substance calculated from the entropy data ($C = T \frac{dS}{dT}$); in the region where the ordering process sets in, there is, of course, a large anomaly in the specific heat which will act in a way similar to the latent heat of a conventional temperature bath.

Thus temperatures have been reached which are very much lower than can be attained simply by the evaporation

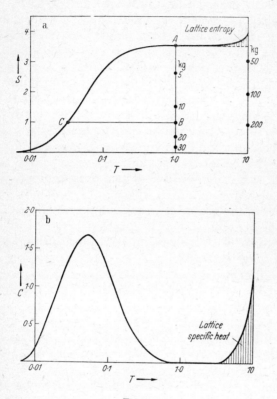

FIG. 5

Simplified sketch of (a) entropy and (b) specific heat of a typical paramagnetic salt.

of helium; it is really only possible to pump helium down to about 0·8° K where its vapour pressure is roughly 10^{-2} mm. At 1/10° K, however, it would be only 10^{-32} mm. and at 3/100° K it would be so small that in a volume as big as our whole galaxy not a single atom would be in equilibrium with liquid helium. It also follows that a gas thermometer cannot be used to determine the temperature; so at last that old relic of the textbooks, the thermodynamic determination of the absolute temperature scale, has been brought into its own.

As we can see from Fig. 5 the lattice energy at $1°$ K has practically disappeared, at least for purposes of thermodynamic calculations. (For example, in iron ammonium alum the lattice entropy at $1°$ is only 10^{-4} of the total entropy.) In this region we have to think of temperature not so much in terms of kinetic energy as in terms of the state of order of some particular part of the system. Now, while the kinetic energy of the lattice atoms must always be characteristic of the equilibrium temperature, it is possible under certain conditions for changes in configuration to become 'frozen-in' in a certain state of disorder, so that different sub-systems of the system possess different 'temperatures'. We find such changes in configuration, for instance, in the ortho-para conversion of hydrogen, in the rearrangement of atoms in a mixed crystal and in the orientation of electronic and nuclear spins. The time effects concerned with the taking up of thermal equilibrium between different parts of such systems actually give rise to some of the most interesting experiments in the low temperature field.

The fact that kinetic energy no longer plays the main role in the definition of temperature recalls the suggestion of replacing the ordinary temperature scale by a $1/T$ or $\log T$ scale; of course the question is not whether this or that scale is the right one but which is more convenient. As the determining factors are now $\Delta U/RT$ terms, it is ratios of temperatures which count, not differences. Obviously then to a low temperature physicist the range from $10°-1°$ is just as significant as the one from $1°-1/10°$, or $1/10°- 1/100°$. It is therefore true that either of these two scales (particularly the logarithmic one) would have some advantages for the low temperature physicist. On the other hand we have to think of the upsetting effect that a change of the temperature scale would have in all other branches of natural science and technology and, if one considers the amount of work necessary to convert all the existing data to a new temperature scale, it is obvious that it would not be worth while. There is one point I would like to emphasize in this connection: absolute zero on either a $(-1/T)$ scale or on the log T scale would become minus infinity. One must resist the temptation to believe that on these scales the law of unattainability of absolute zero would be a triviality. A new law founded on experiment does not of course become subsequently superfluous by a mere mathematical transformation.

Nuclear Paramagnetism

Electronic paramagnetism enables us to reach temperatures of the order of a hundredth or even a few thousandths of a degree, temperatures at which interaction forces bring the system into a state of spontaneous order and therefore put an end to its usefulness as a substance for obtaining still lower temperatures. It has been suggested by GORTER[24] and by KURTI and SIMON[25] that it should be possible to obtain lower temperatures by making use of the nuclear paramagnetism. In this case the interaction forces are bound to be much smaller and it is estimated that temperatures of the order of $1/10,000°-1/100,000°$ K should be attainable. Of course the nuclear dipoles possess much smaller moments and consequently very strong magnetic fields are needed, even if we start at very low temperatures.

Fig. 6 gives an example of the entropy of a nuclear paramagnetic, actually that of one gm. atom of indium; we see that at $1/100°$ K, 100 kilogauss are needed to remove about one-fourth of the entropy due to the disorientation of the nuclear moments. It is therefore clear that we cannot afford to start our demagnetization from temperatures higher than say $1/100°$, and Dr. KURTI is going to tell you something about the difficulties which this involves. In particular, it is necessary to take into account the relaxation time between the spin and lattice systems.

The temperatures attainable by nuclear demagnetization cannot yet be predicted with certainty, but will be of the order of $10^{-4°}$ or $10^{-5°}$ K. At these temperatures the degree of order in the nuclear spin system in zero magnetic field would be the same as at the starting temperature in a strong field, although the particular way in which this order is effected may be different. Now the most interesting experiments envisaged at present in this field are those in which radioactive nuclei are orientated. If this can be achieved, one can expect that the radiation from the ordered nuclei will have a certain, non-uniform, spatial distribution, and this will enable us to obtain information not otherwise

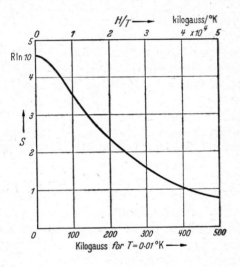

FIG. 6

'Nuclear' entropy of Indium as function of magnetic field at o·o1°K.

available. For some of these experiments it may be simpler to work in a strong field at 'high' temperatures of about 1/100° K than to carry out a second stage of demagnetization from this temperature.

Recently, a number of people have suggested methods of ordering nuclei which, although not applicable in every case, do not require an enormous external magnetic field. Dr. KURTI is going to tell you about this most interesting field of nuclear alignment in which the first results were obtained a short time ago.[26]

Digression Concerning Methods for Attaining Very Low Temperatures

Although I do not intend to discuss matters of technique in this lecture it may be worth while to say a few words concerning the principles involved. The two magnetic methods do, or will, enable us to cover an enormous temperature range below 1°. For the experimenter they have the disadvantage of not being continuous processes and it would certainly be desirable to replace them by continuous ones. KAPITZA[27] has suggested that one such process may be possible by making use of the thermo-mechanical effect in helium II discovered[28] a few years before. If liquid helium II is pushed through a capillary, it comes out at a much reduced temperature (as will be explained in Professor ALLEN's lecture) and this process can in principle be performed continuously. KAPITZA has expressed great hopes for this process and he has suggested that it will be superior to the magnetic method not only from the point of view of convenience but also for reaching still lower temperatures. This conclusion, however, is based on a fallacy, as has been discussed in detail elsewhere.[29] The usefulness of a cooling process does not depend solely on how low a temperature can be reached but also on how much heat the process can absorb at the low temperature in order to take up unavoidable heat influxes, and on how effective it is in cooling down other substances. (In general we wish to cool substances whose physical properties change at low temperatures, and this means that they still have an appreciable amount of entropy left.) Hence the actual form of the entropy curves is very important, and it is clear that the entropy of the working substance should exhibit a large change in the required low temperature region.

Liquid helium below 1°, however, is practically devoid of any entropy and is therefore unsuitable as a working substance at very low temperatures. To compete, for instance, with the magnetic process at 1/100° one would have to circulate some litres of liquid helium per second through about 10^{10} capillaries, and to compete with the nuclear magnetic process, the figures would become astronomical. If a number of rather formidable practical difficulties can be overcome, the helium flow process may turn out to be useful in the region of say $1/2°$ or even a few tenths of a degree, but it certainly will not be able to compete with magnetic processes at lower temperatures, let alone improve on them. These remarks concern only the ordinary helium. At the present moment we know too little about the properties of ^{3}He or mixtures of ^{3}He and ^{4}He to make a definite statement about them. The rareness of the light isotope, however, does not make any process relying on it a very practical proposition.

Thermal Properties of Condensed Phases

The points mentioned so far, most of which you will hear discussed in detail in the following lectures, only concern phenomena observed at very low temperatures. Now there is a danger in concentrating exclusively on work at helium temperatures and this has been accentuated by the advent of the Collins machine which puts liquid helium within reach of anyone who is prepared to pay for it. A large number of important problems can only be properly investigated if the temperature range is extended considerably towards the higher temperatures, and I wish to indicate now a few of these problems.

Probably the most important one concerns the specific heats of the condensed phases. Shortly after the enunciation of the third law a considerable amount of work was done on specific heats particularly to obtain data in order to apply the law to chemical reactions, but comparatively little of it now seems to be reliable. Very often measurements were not continued to low enough temperatures and often only a small number of observations were made, so that, not infrequently, important and unsuspected anomalies in the specific heats were overlooked. In addition we know now that irreversible processes sometimes occur even when pure crystals are cooled down; often these effects can only be noticed if one looks carefully for time effects by repeating the experiments after the substance has been at low temperatures for some time.

It is well known that the relatively few complete investigations in this field have already shown the existence of formerly unsuspected internal transitions. Perhaps the best known are those associated with co-operative phenomena; the anomalous specific heat at the CURIE point of a magnetic substance has for long been recognized as being of this type. It is now known, however, that these co-operative phenomena with their λ type specific heat anomaly are met with in many other systems (as found first in the ammonium salts[30]). In addition there are transitions not of a co-operative type which were predicted by SCHOTTKY[31] and which are quite common in the magnetic region ; the transition in ortho-hydrogen[32] also seems to be of this type. Specific heat measurements are a very direct way of finding out about internal states of excitation; in Fig. 7 I give

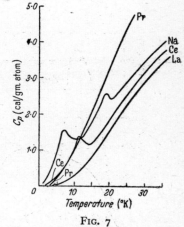

FIG. 7

Atomic heats of four rare earth metals at low temperatures.

the results of recent experiments[33] on some of the rare earth metals. If there were no internal states of excitation, all these curves should be nearly the same as that of lanthanum, so the different course of the curves for cerium, praeseodymium, and neodymium indicate the presence of such states.

Finally, a complete investigation of the specific heat of a substance enables us to find out whether the substance is really in a state of internal equilibrium or 'frozen-in' in some state of disorder. This we may do by comparing the entropy calculated from its specific heats with that derived from a system containing the same particles—but in a different grouping—if the original substance can be transformed reversibly into it by means of a physical or chemical change of state; or by comparing the entropy of the substance with that of its gaseous form, if the entropy of the latter can be derived from spectroscopic data. Experiments of this kind have revealed the great importance of these 'frozen-in' states, and have led, for example, to an elucidation of the nature of a glass.[7, 9] This very wide field, which is at present rather neglected, could offer many opportunities to a discriminating experimentalist.

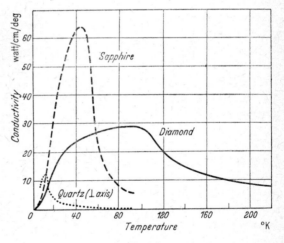

FIG. 8

Thermal conductivities of diamond, sapphire and quartz as function of temperature.

Thermal Conductivity

Until recently little was known about thermal conductivities, particularly of dielectric materials. Only a very few substances have so far been investigated properly by making a complete set of measurements from room temperature to the lowest temperatures attainable. Fig. 8 shows data on the conductivity of diamond, sapphire and quartz[34]. The increase of the conductivity with falling temperature is due to the increase of the mean free path of the heat waves and this can now be explained in sufficient detail by means of the 'Umklapp' process introduced by PEIERLS.[35] The final falling off at the very lowest temperatures in a pure, stress-free crystal is due to the limitations of the mean free path by the external dimensions.[36]

The thermal conductivity, particularly at low temperatures, is extremely sensitive to physical or chemical impurities, which introduce another—and generally most important—source of scattering for the heat waves. Fig. 9 shows the conductivity of a quartz specimen[37] after subjecting it to neutron radiation of different intensities, 1, 2, 3. Even a relatively modest irradiation, causing a dislocation of about 1 in 500 atoms, has the effect of reducing the conductivity at 10° K by a factor of about 500. Thus the study of the thermal conductivity of dielectrics (and metals) over the whole temperature range is a powerful weapon with which to investigate the state

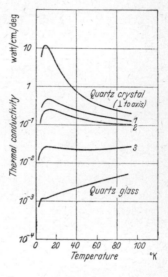

FIG. 9

Thermal conductivities of quartz crystal, neutron-irradiated quartz crystal and quartz glass.

of disorder in a system, whether that disorder be due to impurities or to an intrinsic disorder of the crystal lattice itself.

Mechanical Properties of Solids

Very little is known about these properties at really low temperatures. The few investigations that have been done certainly show that it would be worth while to make a closer investigation of such matters as plasticity, tensile strength and the effect of fatigue. A particularly interesting case should be the investigation of the internal and external friction at very low temperatures.

'Model' Experiments

As I pointed out at the beginning, the main interest of low temperature physics centres around quantum effects, but I would like now to say something about a branch of low temperature work which is quite different: namely the performance of 'model' experiments. Perhaps the best way to explain what I mean is to describe an actual case.

It is of great interest, both for elucidating the structure of matter and for geo-physical applications, to find out how the equilibrium between the solid and the liquid phases changes at very high temperatures and pressures. Owing to the steepness of this equilibrium curve, even the highest pressures so far obtained have not been able to raise the melting temperature of ordinary substances to much more than about that of the critical point. Now analysis of the existing data show that just as it is possible to set up a 'reduced' vapour pressure curve for all fluids, so one can represent melting curves by a 'reduced' melting formula:[38]

$$\frac{p}{\pi} = \left(\frac{T}{T_n}\right)^c - 1$$

T_n is the temperature of the triple point, π is a constant closely related to the internal pressure in the condensed phase and c is a constant about equal to 2. It is thus obvious that in order to raise the melting temperature to very high *reduced* temperatures one should use substances with a low internal pressure.

Substances with low internal pressures are those with small lattice energies, *i.e.* low boiling points. While the internal pressure of a substance melting at room temperature is of the order of 5,000 atm., that of helium is of the order of 10 or 20 atm. (as may be calculated, for instance, from VAN DER WAALS' equation). Thus by using helium as a model substance with which to study the melting process, one can produce the same relative effects with

pressures roughly 300 times smaller than would be necessary if one were making the investigation on a substance
with a melting point at room temperature. Alternatively,
with the same external pressures one is able to penetrate
very much further towards high temperatures. Taking this
as a guiding principle, the melting points of the low boiling
substances have been investigated; the first column of the
table shows the critical temperature of a few substances,
and the second column the melting temperature at a
pressure of 5,000 atm. in terms of the critical temperature.
We see that as predicted by the formula, a given external
pressure will keep a substance in the solid state up to a
temperature which is higher, the lower its boiling point.

	T_{cr}	T_{5000}/T_{cr}
Helium ..	5	7·3
Hydrogen ..	33	2·3
Neon ..	45	1·7
Nitrogen ..	126	1·0
Benzene ..	563	·7

In particular, helium has been solidified at temperatures
of up to 50° K by using a pressure of about 7,500 atm.[39]
This temperature is about ten times the critical one and
corresponds to about fifty times the melting temperature
which helium would exhibit if quantum effects did not
change the picture at low temperatures. Fig. 10 shows the
extrapolated melting temperatures of helium; it suggests
that helium could be solidified at room temperature by a
pressure of about 100,000 atm.—provided that the curve
does not end before then in a new type of critical point
between the solid and the fluid phases. In actual fact the
question whether such a point exists or not is one of the
main interests in these experiments and is a question about
which there are, at present, very few grounds for making
theoretical predictions. It seems to me, however, that if

the matter can ever be settled by experiment, then it will be by using the low boiling substances.

Fig. 11 shows the results of some recent experiments[40] on the entropy differences between the solid and fluid phases of helium; I am showing this to emphasize another advantage of the use of low temperature model experiments. These data have been obtained by measuring the specific heats and the heats of melting at pressures up to 3,000 atmospheres, and so the helium had to be confined

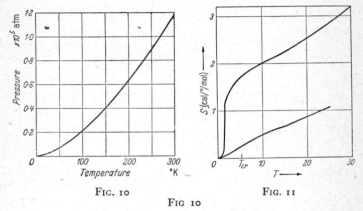

FIG. 10

FIG. 11

FIG. 10

Extrapolated melting curve of helium.

FIG. 11

Entropy of saturated fluid (upper line) and solid (lower line) helium as function of temperature (upper curve fluid phase). The slight kink in the curve of the solid at about 15°K is due to a crystallographic transition.

in very heavy containers. Normally such experiments could not have been carried out in a simple way as the heat capacity of the container would have completely swamped that of the substance we were working on. In our helium experiment, however, the position is quite different. Owing to the small binding forces the specific heat of the helium is relatively high while that of steel at these temperatures is very low; in actual fact it is nearly non-existent—we are working with almost mathematical walls.

These experiments show that the entropy difference between the two phases of helium remains very big up to the highest temperature reached; it is about the same as

that between the phases of
normal substances, although
the entropy of the solid
phase is itself very small
indeed. There is so far no
indication that we are
approaching a solid-fluid
critical point.

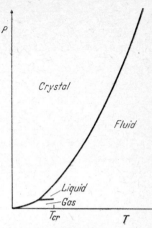

These model experiments
have already proved[38] that
the chief dividing line in the
equilibrium diagram of the
states of aggregation is that
between the crystalline and
the fluid phase as is illustrated in Fig. 12. When
viewed in proper perspec-

Fig. 12

Sketch of the equilibrium diagram
between the states of aggregation.

tive the division between the liquid and gaseous phase
forms only an appendix of very minor importance.

The Unattainability Law Again

I have given you some indications of what the low temperature physicist is at present interested in. Now what can
we expect in the future? While it is premature to point to
some specific problems, I just want to end up with a remark
about the law of unattainability of absolute zero. Is this
law standing in our way when we try to get information
about what happens at still lower temperatures? There was
a law of unattainability implied in the classical picture, but
the unattainability of quantum theory is quite different.
Once the properties of a substance have been measured
down to so low a temperature that it is practically depleted
of its entropy, we can then extrapolate the properties in
question towards lower temperatures.

Now let us suppose that there are going to be some quite
new effects at temperatures lower than those which we
have yet reached. Two questions arise:

(a) Can we with our present knowledge predict the
presence of these effects, even if they are not already

c

indicated by some phenomenon such as paramagnetism?

(b) Will we be able to get temperatures low enough to be able to study them?

The third law—or quantum theory—has given us a means of telling if any entropy is left in a system. Assuming we find that our system still contains some entropy, which it must lose at a still lower temperature, will the unattainability law prevent us from reaching this temperature region and investigating its properties?[41] After what I have explained in this lecture, I do not think I need say very much about this. If something interesting is going to happen, then associated with it there will be a change in the occupation of the energy levels, and the system will lose the corresponding entropy in the temperature region in question. We will be able to get down to the low temperatures by making use of this change in entropy—once we have found a means to influence it—in a similar way to that we have described for a gas and for magnetic dipoles. It will only become progressively more difficult to reduce the temperature when the system has lost practically all its entropy. In this case, only a desert lies before us and so we are not interested in going further: we have already to all extents and purposes a system which is hardly distinguishable from one at absolute zero and its properties can be safely extrapolated. If, on the other hand, some new phenomenon is going to occur at lower temperatures then we will be able to make use of it to reach this oasis of interest. Thus the law of unattainability of absolute zero is no barrier to our knowledge.

To sum up: the characteristic feature of low temperature physics is the fact that quantum laws cause all systems to approach a state of perfect order. There are a variety of ways in which this may come about and the other speakers will discuss in detail some of the more interesting phenomena associated with these ordering processes. I do hope that after having heard all these lectures, you will have felt some of the fascination which this field exerts on its devotees.

REFERENCES

[1] SIMON, F. E.; Science Museum Handbook on Very Low Temperatures, p. 58 (1937);

[2] SIMON, F. E.; Proceedings of the Strasbourg Conference on Magnetism, p. 72 (1939).

[3] EINSTEIN, A.; Ann. Phys. **22**, 180, 800 (1906); **34**, 170 (1911).

[4] DEBYE, P.; Ann. Phys. **39**, 789 (1912).

[5] BORN, M. and VON KÁRMÁN, TH.; Phys. Zeits. **13**, 297 (1912); **14**, 15 (1913).

[6] NERNST, W.; 'Grundlagen des Neuen Waermesatzes' (Halle, 1918).

[7] SIMON, F. E.; Ergebnisse der Exacten Naturwissenschaften **9**, 222 (1930).

[8] See the above, footnote 6, page 226.

[9] JONES, G. O. and SIMON, F. E.; Endeavour, **8**. Oct. 1949.

[10] EUCKEN, A.; 'Lehrbuch der Chemischen Physik' (Leipzig, 1930), p. 58.

[11] FOWLER, R. H. and STERNE, F. E.; Rev. Mod. Phys. **4**, 707 (1932).

[12] SIMON, F. E.; Zeits. f. Phys. **41**, 806 (1927).

[13] SCHOTTKY, W.; 'Thermodynamik' (Berlin, 1929).

[14] FOWLER, F. H. and GUGGENHEIM, E. A.; 'Statistical Mechanics' (Cambridge, 1939), p. 224 ff.

[15] SIMON, F. E.; Physica, **4**, 1089 (1937).

[16] PLANCK, M.; 'Waermestrahlung' (Leipzig, 1906).

[17] LINDEMANN, F. A. and ASTON, F. W.; Phil. Mag. **37**, 523 (1919).

[18] BENNEWITZ, K. and SIMON, F. E.; Zeits. f. Phys. **16**, 183 (1923).

[19] JAMES, R. W., WALLER, I. and HARTREE, D. R.; Proc. Roy. Soc. A. **118**, 334 (1928).

[20] MULLIKEN, R. S., Phys. Rev. **25**, 259, (1925).

[21] NERNST, W.; Zeits. f. Electrochemie, **20**, 357 (1914).

[22] See LONDON, F.; 'Superfluids 1.' New York (1950).

[23] DEBYE, P.; Ann. Phys. **81**, 1154 (1926). GIAUQUE, W. F.; J. Amer. Chem. Soc. **49**, 1864 (1927). See also KURTI, N. and SIMON, F. E.; Naturwissenschaften, **21**, 178 (1933).

[24] GORTER, C. J.; Phys. Zeits. **35**, 923 (1934).

[25] KURTI, N. and SIMON, F. E.; Proc. Roy. Soc. A, **149**, 152 (1935).

[26] DANIELS, J. M.; GRACE, M. A. and ROBINSON, F. N. H.; Nature, **168**, 780, (1951).

[27] KAPITZA, P.; J. Phys. U.S.S.R. **5**, 59 (1941).

[28] DAUNT, J. G. and MENDELSSOHN, K.; Nature, **143**, 719, (1939).

[29] SIMON, F. E.; Physica **16**, 753 (1950).

[30] SIMON, F. E.; Ann. Phys. **68**, 241, (1922).

[31] SCHOTTKY, W.; Phys. Zeits. **22**, 1 (1921); *ibid* **23**, 448 (1922).

[32] SIMON, F. E.; MENDELSSOHN, K. and RUHEMANN, M.; Naturwissenschaften **18**, 34 (1930).

[33] PARKINSON, D. H., SIMON, F. E. and SPEDDING, F. H.; Proc. Roy. Soc. A. **207**, 137, (1951).

[34] BERMAN, R., SIMON, F. E., and WILKS, J.; Nature, **168**, 277, (1951).

[35] PEIERLS, R.; Ann. Phys. **3**, 1055 (1929).

[36] DE HAAS, W. J. and BIERMASZ, Th. Physica, **4**, 752 (1937).

[37] BERMAN, R., KLEMENS, P. G., SIMON, F. E., and FRY, T. M.; Nature, **166**, 864 (1950).

[38] SIMON, F. E.; Trans. Faraday Soc. **33**, 65 (1937).

[39] HOLLAND, F. A., HUGGILL, J. A. W., JONES, G. O. and SIMON, F. E.; Nature **165**, 147 (1950).

[40] DUGDALE, J. S. and SIMON, F. E.; Proc. International Conf. Low Temperature Physics, **25** (1951).

[41] SIMON, F. E.; Science Progress, No. 133 (1939). Reunion Internationale de Physique, Chimie et Biologique (Paris, 1938), p. 11.

THE TEMPERATURE RANGE
BELOW 1° ABSOLUTE

by N. KURTI

Introduction

AFTER PROFESSOR SIMON'S general survey of the problems of low temperature physics you will hear, in the remaining three lectures of this series, about some special low temperature topics. The choice of two of these is fairly obvious as it is reasonable to expect that a lecture each should be devoted to superconductivity and to the striking properties of liquid helium. Both these are 'par excellence' low temperature subjects and deal with phenomena that owe their discovery to the exploration of this new temperature region. It is not so easy, however, to justify the existence of a separate lecture on the temperature region below 1° abs. and I therefore want to explain briefly why this particular temperature region has been singled out for preferential treatment.

There is, after all, nothing that distinguishes, in principle, one hundredth, or one tenth or one degree from say ten, a hundred or a thousand degrees; in fact, the second law of thermodynamics defines the absolute temperature in terms of ratios only. There is, in particular, nothing magical about the number '1' when we talk about one degree absolute, as numbers denoting temperatures have no physical significance and, for instance, the centigrade absolute scale or Kelvin scale (°K) in general use nowadays is simply the result of a convention to divide the interval between the temperature of melting ice and of boiling water into a 100 equal degrees. Why then this place of honour allotted to the temperature range below 1° K?

There are two reasons for this. The first one is somewhat superficial and lies in the novelty of this subject. Experiments down to 80° K, the temperature obtainable with liquid air, have been carried out for nearly seventy years.

The temperature range down to 10° K obtainable by means of condensed hydrogen has been explored for a period only slightly shorter than this, and even the temperature range down to about 1° K which can be obtained by means of liquid helium has been studied for over forty years. But temperatures below 1° K, or to be more precise, temperatures that could not be obtained by means of liquid helium boiling under reduced pressure, have been reached and used in experiments only since 1933. In other words if one deducts the years between 1939 and 1946, during which low temperature research was at a standstill nearly everywhere, this region has been explored for something under ten years.

There is, however, a second and, to my mind, more compelling reason for devoting a separate lecture to this subject. Until 1933 the generation of low temperatures followed roughly the same pattern. It was based on the possibility of cooling and thereby liquefying gases by purely mechanical means. The temperature could then be reduced still further by pumping off the vapour, and by using helium, the gas with the lowest boiling point, a temperature of about 0·7° K was reached in this way first in Leiden[1] and later in other laboratories.

The use of liquefied gases for the generation of low temperatures is a very convenient and powerful method. Continuously running machines can be easily devised, while the industrial techniques for handling gases, and the means of compressing and purifying them, are at the disposal of the low temperature physicist. Moreover, liquefied gases are ideal media for temperature baths. As long as the vapour pressure remains constant the temperature of the bath remains constant, too. Also, thanks to the relatively large heat of evaporation of the liquefied gases, the boiling off of a small quantity of liquefied gas is sufficient either to neutralize an unwanted but usually unavoidable heat influx, or to cool down large pieces of apparatus or specimens.

In order to produce temperatures below those obtainable by means of liquefied gases or to generate cold in this region, fundamentally different methods had to be invented and many of the conventional techniques for experimenting at what one may call standard low temperatures had to be adapted to this new temperature range.

General Considerations

Let us then survey the methods that might be suitable for producing temperatures below those obtainable with liquid helium. In order to do so I will have to recall some of the things you have heard in Professor SIMON'S lecture. The most satisfactory way to explain the production of low temperatures is to consider the entropy or the state of order of the system. In an assembly of atoms or molecules the distribution among the various possible states, characterized by the positions, momenta or any other variables of the particles is determined by the energies of these states. The distribution can be calculated and is given in classical statistics by BOLTZMANN'S formula which states that the probability of finding a particle in a state of energy ϵ is proportional to $e^{-\epsilon/kT}$, where T is the absolute temperature and k is the BOLTZMANN constant. In Fig. 1 the various possible states of a particle (e.g. a gas molecule or an atom in a solid) are represented by the horizontal lines; the vertical distances between them measure the energy differences and the shaded areas indicate the distribution of the particles among these various possible levels at a certain temperature, assumed to be sufficiently high for the particles to be spread over a large number of possible states.* There is thus a certain amount of disorder in this assembly, and, according to what you heard last week, such a system could, in principle, be used for cooling. In practice one must find some external variable such as, for instance, pressure or magnetic field or electric field (X in the figure), by means of which the energy levels may be shifted. Let us assume that by changing this external variable from X_1 to X_2 one increases the energy difference between the states. Then, if the temperature remains constant, the

---

* Strictly speaking each line represents a large but constant number of states. The varying distances between these lines indicate that the states get closer as their energy increases. Similarly, the shaded areas represent the populations within the corresponding energy intervals.

atoms will tend to crowd into the lower energy levels in accordance with BOLTZMANN's relation, the distribution will be less spread out, the order will be greater. In the language of thermodynamics we have reduced the entropy of this system isothermally.

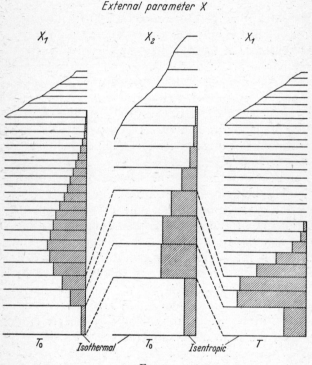

FIG. 1.

Cooling process represented in the energy level diagram.

What will happen if we now thermally insulate the system and change this variable X in the opposite direction and so bring it back to its original value, thereby restoring the original energy scheme? As there is no heat exchange with the exterior $(dQ = O)$ the entropy that is the state of order, will remain the same during this process $(dS = dQ/T = O)$, provided of course that the transformation is reversible. Now, for the state of order, and hence for the distribution to the various levels to remain the same while the distance between the energy levels gets reduced, the temperature must fall in the same proportion.

It is instructive to calculate by means of this reasoning the cooling produced by the adiabatic expansion of an ideal monatomic gas. According to quantum theory the translational motion of gas molecules in a closed space is quantized, that means the kinetic energy can only change in finite steps. It is true that the distances between the energy levels are so small compared with the energy of thermal agitation kT at temperatures where gases exist, that one is permitted to assume a continuous energy spectrum. Nevertheless, one can calculate the energy terms and one finds that the energy of a given state r is inversely proportional to the 2/3 power of the volume occupied by the gas: $\varepsilon_r \propto (r/V)^{2/3}$.

If one expands the gas, the spacing between the energy levels will be reduced proportionally to $1/V^{2/3}$. If the expansion is isentropic, the state of order, i.e. the distribution among the various levels, remains the same. This means that the BOLTZMANN factor, which determines the distribution, must remain constant during this process, and hence the temperature must fall in the same ratio as the separation of the energy levels. We thus find that for this process $TV^{2/3} = $ const, which is, of course, the well-known formula $TV^{\gamma-1} = $ const, for the adiabatic expansion of an ideal gas, the ratio of the specific heats γ being equal to 5/3 for a monatomic gas. Fig. 1 was actually drawn to illustrate this process, the external parameter X being the volume, and $X_1 > X_2$.

What then are the methods for attaining temperatures out of reach of the standard method of gas liquefaction, that is, below the lowest temperature obtainable with liquid helium? I will first of all describe briefly two methods which, although not yet properly tried out, might find some application in reaching this temperature region. You will probably hear more about these methods and their theoretical treatment in the following two lectures because one of them uses superconductors and the other one uses liquid helium. This is not surprising, since the inset of superconductivity is characterized by fundamental changes in the electric and magnetic properties, while in the case of liquid helium, some very striking flow-characteristics develop at sufficiently low temperatures. Both these effects are bound to be connected with the redistribution among the various possible states of the particles in question, namely the metal-electrons and the helium atoms respectively. It is therefore likely, that if only we can influence these properties by some external means, a way might be opened for attaining lower temperatures.

Let us look first at the superconducting method.[2] As I said before, the disappearance of electrical resistance is accompanied by a change in magnetic properties. In the superconducting state the metal behaves like a strongly diamagnetic substance; one might call it a perfect diamagnetic as the magnetic lines of force are altogether pushed out, and the magnetic induction becomes zero inside a superconductor. But even below the so-called transition temperature for superconductivity, it is possible to bring the substance back to its normal state by an external magnetic field, the value of which depends on the temperature. Although a detailed theory of the mechanism of superconductivity is still lacking, there exists a satisfactory thermodynamical treatment of these effects. Fig. 2 shows the entropy of tantalum which becomes superconductive at 4·4°K. Strictly speaking the figure represents the entropy of the conduction electrons in tantalum, but it so happens that the entropy due to the vibrations of the atoms in the crystal lattice is small compared with this electronic contribution. Above the transition point the entropy is practically independent of the magnetic field. If the magnetic field is large enough to destroy superconductivity, the entropy curve continues even below the transition point its trend at higher temperatures. In zero field or in a field smaller than this critical field H_c the entropy is lower, that means that in the superconducting state the electrons are more ordered than in the normal state. One can see straight away how these properties can be used for lowering the temperature. Let us, for instance, take tantalum at 2° K and in zero field, that is in the superconductive, more ordered state and then increase the field slowly. Nothing happens until the critical field is reached, and then suddenly the substance passes from the superconducting into the normal state. If this process is carried out adiabatically, the state of order must remain the same and hence the

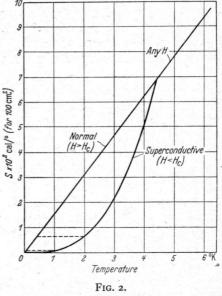

FIG. 2.
Entropy of tantalum.

substance will cool until a temperature (0·4° K in this case) is reached, at which the entropy in the normal state is the same as the entropy in the superconducting state at the starting temperature. Starting from a lower temperature, say, from 1° K, one should reach 0·07° K.

This method commends itself on various grounds. For instance, the necessary magnetic fields are small, only about 1,000 gauss or so; also, the use of a metal as cooling agent may solve some of the difficulties of heat contact at low temperatures. Against these are to be set, however, some disadvantages. One is that the cooling is produced by turning on a magnetic field and one might have to carry out measurements at the low temperature in a field of 1,000 gauss or so, which in many cases may be undesirable. Another, more important, disadvantage is that although large drops in temperature might be achieved, only small quantities of heat are involved, and the small heat capacities would make it difficult to maintain the low temperature one has reached. I will discuss this point later in comparison with the cooling process by adiabatic demagnetization of paramagnetic salts.

The use of liquid helium for cooling has been discussed by Professor SIMON, so I only need mention it briefly. You will hear in more detail from Professor ALLEN that below 2·2° K liquid helium has various striking properties such as vanishing viscosity and extremely large heat conductivity, and that these can be roughly correlated if one imagines that at low temperatures liquid helium is a mixture of two types of fluids. The 'superfluid' component has zero entropy and by separating it from the bulk liquid one should obtain a substance that is very much colder than the original liquid. This separation can be affected by forcing the liquid through a filter with very fine holes; for instance, a tube tightly packed with fine powder which offers great flow resistance to the normal component but lets the superfluid component pass through with small hindrance. Just as in the case of cooling by superconductors one can predict the effect, and one finds that although the actual lowering of temperatures can be quite important, the smallness of the heat capacities rules out this method for most practical purposes. There remains then the magnetic cooling method to which I want to devote the rest of my talk.

The Magnetic Cooling Method

(a) Theoretical Basis

As we have seen before, a system to be used for cooling at the starting temperature must be in a certain state of disorder which is capable of reduction by external means.

The disorder of atoms or ions and molecules can be due not only to positions or to velocities but also to orientation, if a vector, such as a magnetic or an electric dipole is associated with the particle. Let us then consider an assembly of such dipoles. If we assume that they do not interact with each other or with other atoms or molecules surrounding them, then in the absence of an external field, magnetic or electric, all possible orientations have the same energy; they are all equally probable and hence with regard to orientation the disorder is as complete as can be.

This is, of course, a very idealized picture, because one cannot talk about perfectly free and non-interacting dipoles especially not if one deals with solids where the ions or atoms or molecules are closely packed. Actually, the energies associated with the various orientations are slightly different, but provided the energy differences are very small compared with kT, the distribution among the various states calculated by BOLTZMANN's formula will be uniform and the system will be in complete disorder. If, on the other hand, these energy differences are comparable with, or larger than kT, there will be a crowding in the lower lying states, the system will be more or less ordered and not particularly suitable for the production of low temperatures. This explains why the use of electric dipoles has to be ruled out as a cooling method. Electric dipoles, as you know, are rigidly anchored to the molecule or to a group of atoms in the molecule and their orientation must be accompanied by the rotation of the molecule or group of atoms as a whole. But this cannot happen at low temperatures because of the very strong forces acting between the molecules in a solid, and even at the relatively high temperatures of liquid air or liquid hydrogen, electric dipoles are in an ordered (or 'frozen-in' disordered) state brought about by these interaction forces.

The position is different with magnetic dipoles. They are associated with the individual electrons within the atom or ion and so in many cases retain their freedom of orientation even in the solid state. You probably will have heard of the famous experiments of KAMERLINGH ONNES and

WOLTJER[3] carried out in Leiden in 1924, which clearly showed that the magnetic properties of gadolinium sulphate followed closely the course predicted by LANGEVIN's theory based on complete freedom of the individual magnetic dipoles. When I say completely free, I mean, of course, that the small energy differences associated with different orientation in the absence of an external magnetic field are very small compared with the thermal energy kT. It was the 'ideal' behaviour of gadolinium sulphate even at liquid helium temperatures that led DEBYE[4] and GIAUQUE[5] to suggest, independently of each other, the use of such paramagnetic salts for producing very low temperatures.

Let us then represent the properties of such an ideal or nearly ideal paramagnetic solid in our energy diagram (Fig. 3). For the purpose of this diagram I assumed that the individual magnetic ions have an angular momentum $\mathcal{J} = 5/2$ with which is associated a magnetic moment of $\mathcal{J}g\beta$ where β is the BOHR magneton, the elementary magnetic moment, and g the so called splitting factor which indicates to what extent the resultant angular momentum $\mathcal{J}$ is due to the orbital motion of the electron and to its own spin. According to quantum theory an angular momentum $\mathcal{J}$ has $2\mathcal{J} + 1$ possible orientations relative to an axis of quantization, such as an external magnetic field or a crystalline axis. Thus in the present case we have six states for each ion corresponding to these six orientations and you see the six lines representing the energies of these states. If the magnetic dipoles were completely free these six lines would coincide; in reality there are energy differences U, but I will assume that these are small compared with kT and that, therefore, according to BOLTZMANN's law the ions are equally distributed among these six states. Accordingly, the heavy black lines representing the number of ions occupying each level are equal.

What happens if we bring such an assembly of magnetic dipoles, maintained at a constant temperature, into a magnetic field H? Obviously the energies of the states corresponding to the different relative orientations of the magnetic dipoles and the magnetic field will be different. A dipole pointing in the same direction as the magnetic field has a lower potential energy than a dipole pointing in the opposite direction. Our energy levels which in the absence of the field almost coincided, are now separated by differences equal to $g\beta H$ (in most cases of practical interest $g\beta H \gg U$), and according to BOLTZMANN'S formula the distribution will change and more ions will go into the lower energy levels which correspond to the dipoles pointing in

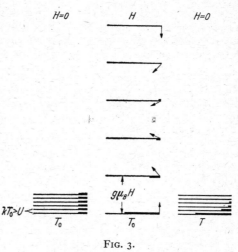

FIG. 3.
Energy diagram of a paramagnetic ion.

the direction of the external field. The substance becomes magnetized and at the same time gets more ordered corresponding to this preferential occupation of the lower levels. As you see, the distribution and hence the intensity of magnetization and the entropy depends only on $g\beta H/kT$, i.e. on H/T.

What happens if after thermally insulating the paramagnetic salts we remove the external magnetic field, that is, perform an isentropic demagnetization during which the state of order must remain the same? We know that in the absence of an external field the energy differences U between the state corresponding to various orientations are very small. If then, in spite of the smallness of U the degree of order and hence the distribution is to remain the same, it is necessary for the temperature to drop until the value of U/kT is the same as $g\beta H/kT_o$ (where T_o and T are the initial and final temperatures respectively). We thus have the following roughly quantitative expression for the cooling to be expected in an adiabatic demagnetization: $T/T_o = $ const. (U/H) or, to express it in words: the final temperature reached after adiabatic demagnetization from a field H to a field zero is such that at this temperature the degree of order produced by the internal interaction forces is the same as that produced by the external magnetic field H at the initial temperature.

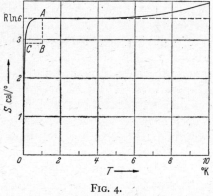

FIG. 4.
Entropy of a paramagnetic ion.

It is instructive to represent this process in the entropy diagram and Fig. 4 shows the entropy in a zero external magnetic field, of one gram ion of iron ammonium alum, one of the salts most commonly used for the magnetic cooling method. As you see, in the temperature range between 0·3° K and 5° K the entropy has a constant value of $R \times \log 6$ (R being the gas constant) corresponding to the six energetically equivalent and thus equally probable orientations of the ferric ion. It is entirely due to the randomness of these dipole orientations as the contribution of the lattice vibrations to the entropy becomes negligible below about 5° K. At higher temperatures, where the lattice vibrations get appreciably excited, they too contribute to the entropy and this explains the increase in entropy which becomes noticeable above 5° K. At sufficiently low temperatures (about 0·3° K in this case) the entropy drops indicating the establishment of order with respect to the dipole orientations. This occurs in the temperature region where kT is of the same order of magnitude as the spread of the energy levels into which the various orientations are resolved by interaction forces.

If one has this sort of entropy curve at one's disposal and if one knows the entropy change produced by isothermal application of a magnetic field at the starting temperature, one can predict the temperature reached after adiabatic demagnetization. Thus one sees that in this particular substance a starting field of 10 Kgauss leads from an initial temperature of 1° K to a final temperature of 0·05° K. This diagram will also show you clearly the two reasons why the magnetic method of cooling can be used only at fairly low temperatures. The first reason is that if one started at a higher temperature at which the entropy of the lattice is no longer negligible, one would have to pull down a big thermal ballast to the low temperature with resulting loss of efficiency. Secondly, the degree of order produced by isothermal magnetizations, that means the magnitude of the entropy reduction, depends on the ratio of magnetic field to temperature, and thus 100 Kgauss would be necessary to produce at 10° K the same entropy change as that produced by 10 Kgauss at 1° K.

(b) Experimental Realization

Although the first suggestion of the magnetic cooling method by DEBYE[4] and by GIAUQUE[5] was made in 1926, it was not till 1933 that the theory was put into practice, by GIAUQUE and McDOUGALL[6] in Berkeley, California, and by DE HAAS, WIERSMA and KRAMERS[7] in Leiden, Holland. Before going into experimental details, let us see the main outline of the experimental procedure. In Fig. 5 the three essential phases in a magnetic cooling process are represented schematically. The specimen, usually in the shape of an ellipsoid or sphere so that its magnetic properties may be easily calculated, is in a space filled with helium gas at a pressure of a few hundredths of a mm Hg. This ensures good thermal contact between the salt and the surrounding bath of liquid helium boiling under a reduced pressure and thus kept at a temperature of about 1° K. The various necessary thermal shields at liquid hydrogen or liquid air temperature which surround this cryostat are, for simplicity's sake, omitted. The specimen is magnetized at the constant temperature of the bath by means of an electromagnet represented by the two pole pieces,

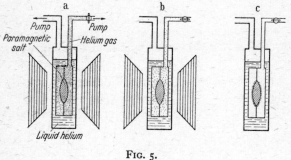

FIG. 5.
The magnetic cooling method.

(Fig. 5 (a)) and the accompanying heat of magnetization is absorbed through evaporation by the liquid helium bath. Next the specimen is thermally insulated by pumping out the helium gas surrounding it (Fig. 5 (b)). Finally the magnet is removed (Fig. 5(c)) and this isentropic demagnetization results in a cooling of the specimen. You will notice that in (b) I indicated by means of a few dots that there was a finite gas pressure in the container before demagnetization, while the absence of dots in (c) indicates perfect vacuum. This is explained by the fact that the specimen usually reaches such a low temperature that the vapour pressure of helium becomes negligible (e.g. 10^{-11} mm Hg at 0·3° K), and hence acts as an exceedingly powerful

D

pump absorbing the residual gas. Fig. 6 shows in some detail the arrangement used in a number of apparatus in Oxford. The specimen which, according to the apparatus or the type of experiments, is usually between 5 and 12 mm in diameter and a few cm long, weighing anything between 1 and 20 gms is tautly suspended on silk or nylon fibres inside a cylindrical metallic cage which slides into the inner space of the cryostat. This space is closed off by means of a greased ground joint and connected to a vacuum pump by means of tube A while the surrounding helium bath is pumped by means of tube B. Another evacuated space isolates the cryostat thermally from the bath of liquid hydrogen which also contains a set of coils whose mutual inductance depends on the magnetic susceptibility of the specimen and thus permits the measurement of this quantity either by means of a ballistic galvanometer or by means of an A.C. bridge.

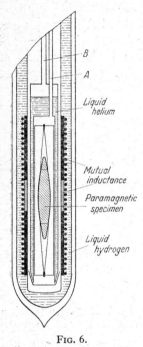

B

A

Liquid helium

Mutual inductance

Paramagnetic specimen

Liquid hydrogen

Fig. 6.
Demagnetization cryostat

Our simple formula $T = \text{const}$ $T_o\,(U/H_o)$ shows directly that the final temperature reached by demagnetization is determined by the starting field H_o, starting temperature T_o, and the magnitude of the internal interaction energy (U). This interaction energy is, of course, different for different substances, and we will see more about its nature and magnitude when we discuss the properties of these paramagnetic salts. But, for a given substance, the final temperature is the lower the higher the value of the ratio H_o/T_o.

The starting temperature T_o is usually that of the surrounding liquid helium bath, and all I need say here is

Fig. 7.
Adiabatic demagnetization with the Bellevue Magnet.

Fig. 8.
Adiabatic demagnetization with the Bellevue Magnet.

FIG. 9.

The 1,000 kW Magnet coil of the Clarendon Laboratory

that it is quite feasible, even without the use of powerful pumps,[8] to reach about 0·8° K with liquid helium boiling under reduced pressure. As to the magnetizing field, it must fulfil two conditions. It must be capable of being kept on for periods of up to an hour or so, and the pole-gap or, in the case of a solenoid, the cavity must be large enough (20 cc is about the minimum) to accommodate the relevant part of the cryostat. For fields up to about 15 Kgauss these conditions are satisfied by moderate sized laboratory electro-magnets, and difficulties arise only when one wishes to go up to fields of 25 or 50 Kgauss.

There are, broadly speaking, two ways of doing this. One is to use a very large iron-cored electro-magnet with a core diameter of as much as $\frac{1}{2}$ or 1 metre and then to concentrate the magnetic flux into the pole-gap by means of tapered pole pieces. An example of a magnet of this type is the famous 100-ton electro-magnet of the French Academy of Sciences, designed by Professor COTTON[9] and housed near Paris in the Bellevue laboratories of the Centre National de la Recherche Scientifique. This is perhaps the most versatile and universal magnet in existence. It is installed in such a way that quite bulky apparatus can be moved close to or actually into the pole gap; thus when it was used for demagnetization experiments[10] a complete helium liquefier was mounted on a trolley (see Figs. 7 and 8) and in this way the cryostat could be brought into the pole-gap or taken far away from it according to the phase of the experiment.

The other method of producing intense magnetic fields relies on effectively cooled solenoids dissipating large electric power of the order of 1,000 kW. This method has been particularly developed by BITTER[11] in the United States and by TSAI[12] in France, and Fig. 9 shows a solenoid now installed in the Clarendon Laboratory which with a power of 1,000 kW produces 50 Kgauss over a volume of about 100 cm^3. The main problem in this case is how to absorb the heat produced, and this is done by pumping cooling water at the rate of about 1,000 litres/min. through the solenoid.

The most striking difference between these two methods is in the relative sizes of the actual magnet and the motor generator furnishing the current. In the case of the iron-cored magnet the output from a smallish generator (25–100 kW) is fed into a magnet weighing 10 to 100 tons, while with the other method the solenoid itself weighs only a few hundred pounds, and it is the weight of the generator that is counted in tens of tons.

The Temperature Scale Below 1° K

We next come to the question of how the temperature reached after demagnetization may be determined; a comparison with the gasthermometric method of temperature measurement is very illuminating. For an ideal gas the absolute temperature is proportional to the pressure, but even for a gas whose behaviour is not quite ideal, the absolute temperature can be determined from its pressure provided the deviations from the ideal gas law are known and can be allowed for. The position is similar for the paramagnetic substances we are concerned with. For an ideal paramagnetic substance, that is, for one in which the magnetic dipoles are perfectly free, CURIE's law postulates that the magnetic susceptibility is inversely proportional to the absolute temperature. Hence by measuring the susceptibility one can determine the absolute temperature. If the interaction forces in the paramagnetic salt are not negligible, but if their magnitude and their nature is known, one can, by applying corrections, still calculate the absolute temperature. This method, however, usually breaks down when temperatures are reached at which kT is of the order of the interaction energy. As the magnetic cooling method takes one into this very temperature range some means have had to be found for determining the temperature, and the obvious and only sure method is that based on the second law of thermodynamics.

Fig. 10 shows how this is done in practice. Let point A represent the entropy of a certain quantity of a paramagnetic salt at the temperature T_o and in an external magnetic field H_1. If we increase the magnetic field from

H_1 to H_2, the temperature remaining constant, an amount
of heat ΔQ_o will be evolved, which can be determined
experimentally, e.g. by measuring the quantity of helium
evaporating from the surrounding bath. As the temperature T_o is known in the absolute scale, the entropy change
ΔS can be calculated by the relation $\Delta S = \Delta Q_o/T_o$ and
we can plot point B representing the entropy of the paramagnetic salt in a field H_2 at T_o.

Let us now consider the two isentropic demagnetizations
to zero field, one from A and the other from B represented
by the two lines parallel to the axis of temperatures and

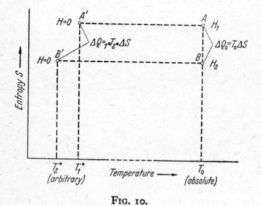

FIG. 10.
Determination of the thermodynamic temperature scale.

leading to points A' and B'. While normally we cannot
rely on calculating the absolute temperature from the susceptibilities, we can still define an arbitrary temperature
scale based on the susceptibility, e.g. by CURIE's law.
We will mark by means of an asterisk temperatures in this
arbitrary CURIE scale $T^* = C/\kappa$ (κ = susceptibility C =
CURIE constant), and thus T_1^* in this CURIE-scale corresponds to point A' and T^*_2 to B'. You will notice that the
axis of temperatures contains a dotted portion; the temperatures to right of this region are absolute temperatures,
while those to the left are in the arbitrary scale. Let us now
heat the specimen, e.g. electrically or by irradiation with

γ-rays from the arbitrary temperature T_2^* to the arbitrary temperature T_1^* and let the necessary amount of heat be ΔQ. The entropy difference between point A' and B' is, of course, the same as that between A and B and consequently we can write $\Delta Q = {}_1^*T_2^* \Delta S$ where the symbol ${}_1^*T_2^*$ denotes the absolute temperature corresponding to a temperature intermediate between T_1^* and T_2^* in the arbitrary scale. Eliminating ΔS between the two expressions we get for the absolute temperature the following expression ${}_1^*T_2^* = T_o (\Delta Q / \Delta Q_o)$. Clearly, if instead of just two demagnetizations we perform a series of demagnetizations from sufficiently close values of the magnetic field, we can finally get an accurate correlation between the absolute temperatures and the temperatures in our arbitrary scale.

As you see, the method is very simple in principle, but there are a number of experimental difficulties mainly connected with the uniform and measurable introduction of heat to the specimen at the low temperature. These difficulties have been overcome and experiments in Oxford,[13] Leiden[14] and in Berkeley[15] resulted in such correlation between the absolute temperature scale and the arbitrary CURIE scale being obtained for a number of paramagnetic salts down to a temperature of 0·004° K. Fig. 11 shows such a typical correlation curve, the one for iron ammonium alum. As you see at temperatures above about 0·2° K there is no great difference between T^* and T. At lower temperatures the arbitrary temperature scale shows higher values than the absolute scale that means the susceptibility increases less rapidly with falling temperature than predicted by CURIE's law. At about 0·04° K there is an abrupt change; the temperature in the CURIE scale drops rapidly in a narrow temperature interval of the absolute scale which means there is a sudden marked increase in susceptibility. At still lower temperatures T^* actually increases with decreasing absolute temperature that means the susceptibility as a function of the absolute temperature passes through a maximum. This behaviour shows clearly how wrong it would have been to regard the temperature derived from the susceptibility by CURIE's Law as the absolute temperature. We would then have had the obviously absurd phenomenon of heat input resulting in a decrease of temperature, that means a substance with a negative specific heat.

The Properties of Paramagnetic Salts Below 1° K

As mentioned before, the ordering process of the elementary magnets in the paramagnetic salt is governed by the type and magnitude of forces acting on them and thus the

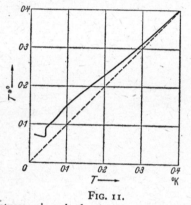

FIG. 11.

'Curie' temperature against absolute temperature for iron ammonium alum.

knowledge of the temperature variation of the entropy, which is a measure of the disorder, might enable one to learn something about these interaction forces. In Fig. 12 is shown the entropy as function of the absolute temperature for three of the most commonly used paramagnetic salts. These curves follow directly from the experiments to establish the absolute temperature scale described above and are based on work done in Oxford[13] and in Leiden[14]. At high temperatures the entropies approach constant, temperature independent values, $R \log 6$ for iron ammonium alum and manganese ammonium sulphate corresponding to the six possible orientations of ferric and manganous ions (angular momentum $\mathcal{J} = 5/2$) and $R \log 4$ for chromium potassium alum ($\mathcal{J} = 3/2$). In all three cases, as we go to lower temperatures, we observe a smooth, gradual falling off of the entropy occurring at the highest temperature in the manganese salt, at a slightly lower one in the chrome alum and at a still lower one in iron alum. The cause of this drop is shown by theoretical considerations to be the influence of the non-uniform electrical field of the crystalline lattice on these magnetic ions which results in slightly different energy levels corresponding to the various relative orientation of the magnetic dipoles and the crystalline axis. At sufficiently high temperatures there is practically equal distribution, and only when we get into

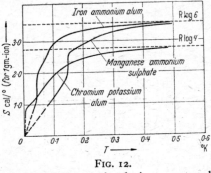

FIG. 12.
Entropies of paramagnetic salts in zero external field.

the temperature range where kT becomes comparable with the separation of the levels, do we get a redistribution of the magnetic ions and a drop in entropy corresponding to the increased order. The smoothness of this part of the curve is consistent with the picture of each individual magnetic ion being practically independent from its neighbours and mainly being acted upon by the crystalline field.

From these S—T curves one can deduce the nature and the magnitude of this crystalline splitting of the energy levels and for a time adiabatic demagnetization was the most reliable method for obtaining information about very small splittings. More recently, however, the application of microwave spectroscopy to paramagnetic salts[16] has provided a more powerful tool, and, in fact, paramagnetic resonance measurements enable one now to predict the temperature variation of the entropy, in so far as it is caused by crystalline splitting.

It follows from theory that, for the magnetic ions we are concerned with, an electric field cannot establish complete order and that the final reduction of the entropy to zero can be brought about only by direct interaction between the dipoles. Indeed, as we go to still lower temperatures we notice an abrupt drop in the entropy which occurs at different temperatures for different substances and is a sign of some sort of self-alignment of the magnetic dipoles. From the known magnetic moments and their relative distances one can calculate their magnetic interaction energy, and one finds that the corresponding characteristic temperatures lie between 0·01° and 0·1° K. Thus a purely magnetic interaction between the elementary magnets could be responsible for this ordering process.

Before discussing the phenomena appearing at this temperature, let us first consider how these entropy curves give us practical information about the way to choose substances for different types of adiabatic demagnetization experiments. If we assume, for instance, that the aim is to reach a very low temperature, then a substance is needed for which the drop in entropy occurs at the lowest possible temperature, that means one with the lowest interaction energy. Now the energy of interaction with the crystalline field depends mainly on the symmetry of the immediate surroundings of the paramagnetic ion and the corresponding characteristic temperature can be reduced to well below 0·1° K by choosing a suitable substance. The dipole-dipole interactions which depend on the magnitude and relative distance of the dipoles can be influenced more directly. For instance, comparing chrome alum and iron alum, two substances with almost identical dipole separations, we see that the steep drop in entropy occurs at a lower temperature in the former substance than in the latter one, probably because the magnetic moment of the Cr^{+++} ion is smaller than that of the Fe^{+++} ion. On the other hand, for a given magnetic moment the interaction may be reduced by 'magnetic dilution', i.e. increased dipole-dipole distances. For example, one can choose a substance in which the paramagnetic ion is in a large molecule, or one can form a mixed crystal of the paramagnetic salt with an isomorphous diamagnetic salt. Probably the lowest temperature yet reached ($0.0015°$ K) was obtained in Leiden[17] by means of a mixed crystal containing one part chromium potassium alum to twenty parts of aluminium potassium alum.

If the emphasis is not on reaching a very low temperature but rather on maintaining the specimen for as long a time as possible at some given temperature, then the choice will fall on a substance which has a high specific heat C, or (because $C = T\,dS/dT$) a marked entropy drop at the required temperature. Referring again to Fig. 12, iron alum is more suitable for experiments in the temperature region round $0.04°$ K than chrome alum, although for reaching very low temperatures the latter is to be preferred. The statistical interpretation of these specific heat anomalies which, as we shall see later, are of considerable practical importance for the magnetic

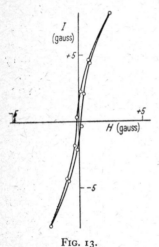

FIG. 13.
Hysteresis cycle of iron ammonium alum at $0.03°$K.

cooling method, becomes clear if one remembers that whenever the entropy, i.e. the state of order, changes there is a rearrangement of the paramagnetic ions among the different energy levels. Increase in temperature brings about an increase in the population of the higher energy levels, and the heat capacity is due to the additional energy required to lift particles into the higher states.

I want to say a few words about the phenomena occurring below the temperature at which direct interaction forces compel the dipoles into an ordered state. Fig. 13 shows a magnetization cycle obtained with iron ammonium alum at about 0·03° K and we see a characteristic hysteresis curve with finite remanence and coercive force[18]. Remembering that, as I mentioned before, the susceptibility increases substantially in a narrow temperature range, there is a certain analogy between the behaviour of these paramagnetic salts below what one may call their CURIE points and that of ordinary ferromagnetic materials such as iron or nickel, but whether this analogy is more than a superficial one is by no means certain. In particular, the remanences are very much smaller than they would be if after removal of the magnetic field a large proportion of the magnetic dipoles pointed in the same direction, and it is still an open question whether this is a case of ferromagnetism in which the parallel orientation of the dipoles represents the stable state, or of so-called anti-ferromagnetism characterized by an ordered anti-parallel orientation of the dipoles.[19] It may well be that in these cases one is no longer justified in describing a substance as ferromagnetic or antiferromagnetic, and that even for a given substance the type of order is determined by the magnitude of a small external magnetic field or by the shape of the specimen. This latter effect is due to the fact that the interaction forces, represented phenomenologically as a molecular field, are of the same order as the demagnetizing field produced by the free magnetic poles on the surface of the specimen. Some of the recent experimental and theoretical work[20] represents an important step towards the solution of this question, which is certainly one of the most interesting problems arising out of the magnetic cooling method.

Thermal Insulation and Thermal Contact. Some Experiments Below 1° K

Interesting as the study of the properties of these paramagnetic salts is, the chief merit of the magnetic cooling method is that it enables us to cool other systems to temperatures below 1° K, so that their behaviour may be studied. This brings us to the question of how to cool

other substances to these temperatures and how to maintain them there, in other words, to the problem of thermal
contact and thermal insulation.

Good thermal insulation which enables one to keep a
cold specimen or apparatus for a long period of time at a
temperature different from its surroundings is of paramount
importance in low temperature work. To overcome thermal
leaks is, on the technical side, one of the greatest preoccupa-
tions of low temperature physicists, and it may therefore
seem paradoxical that the problem of thermal insulation
at the very low temperatures we are dealing with is actually
easier to solve than at somewhat higher temperatures. That
this should be so, becomes clear if we consider how the
two main causes of heat influx, namely radiation and
conduction behave at these temperatures. Radiation from
surroundings kept at $1°$ K is negligible, because it falls off
with the fourth power of the absolute temperature. As to
conduction, the heat conductivities of solids which may be
used for supporting or suspending specimens (e.g. glass,
fibres, alloys) are small and diminish with falling temperature, while gas conduction may be neglected because of the
smallness of the vapour pressures. As a result extremely
good thermal insulation can be achieved in this temperature
range[21], and, for instance, the heat influx to a cooled paramagnetic salt specimen can be reduced without too much
trouble to about 1 erg/min/cm^2. It is interesting to note
that to benefit fully from such good thermal insulation one
must even eliminate mechanical vibrations, which through
frictional energy dissipation can generate heat at a rate
many times higher than the heat leak.[22, 36]

Low heat influx is, of course, not all that is needed, as
the rate of temperature rise also depends on the heat
capacity of the specimen, and as you know, one of the main
difficulties of calorimetric experiments at low temperatures
lies in the extreme smallness of most specific heats. But
here again the very nature of the magnetic cooling method
makes conditions more favourable as the anomalous specific heats of the paramagnetic salts I mentioned before are
truly formidable when compared with the normal lattice

specific heats or electronic specific heats. Thus, for instance, the heat capacity of 10 gm of iron ammonium alum at 0·05 K is about the same as that of a quarter of a ton of copper or twenty litres of liquid helium at the same temperature.

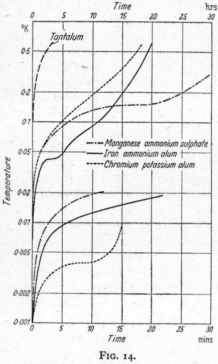

FIG. 14.
Warming rates for various substances.

Fig. 14 shows that the combination of good thermal insulation and large specific heats gives rise to very slow heating-up rates. The curves refer to specimens of various paramagnetic salts of about 5 cm³ volume (say ellipsoids of 12 mm diameter and 80 mm length), and we see that even with the generously large heat influx of 5 erg/min /cm² assumed for this calculation, the temperature rises are so slow that it is possible to carry out almost isothermal experiments at these low temperatures. Fig. 14 also shows the calculated heating-up rate of a tantalum specimen cooled by means of the superconducting method. In order to have a fair comparison, a much larger volume of tantalum than of salt was assumed (100 cm^3 instead of 5 cm^3) as the super-conducting method of cooling requires small magnetic fields and hence one could tolerate larger dimensions. Below 0·1° K the superconducting method is, from the point of view of warming-up markedly inferior to the magnetic method, but in the temperature range between 0·2° K and 1° K it offers an attractive alternative, even if we take into account the existence of paramagnetic sub-stances with high specific heats between 0·2° K and 1° K, which are therefore more suitable for work in this tempera-ture range.

If one wants to do experiments at these low temperatures on other substances, they must be cooled by means of a paramagnetic salt, and the question of thermal contact arises. The use of gas as a heat transmitting agent is, of course, out of the question, and there remain the possi-bilities of heat transfer by direct mechanical contact or by means of a liquid (helium in our case) as an inter-mediary.

Taking first the method by solid contact the simplest and most effective way is to mix the substance one wants to cool with the salt used as cooling agent and then com-press this mixture to form a solid 'pill'. This method has been used, for instance, in investigations on supercon-ductivity, and among the exhibits you will see a pill of granulated cadmium imbedded in iron ammonium alum which served in the experiments that showed that cadmium becomes superconducting at 0·54° K.[23] It might seem sur-prising at first sight that the inset of superconductivity could be detected on such a specimen, but you must remember that the disappearance of electrical resistance is accompanied by a very marked change in the magnetic susceptibility, and therefore by measuring the total induced magnetic moment of the specimen as a function of tempera-ture the transition point could be found. If one wants to separate the superconductor from the cooling agent, or if, for instance, one wants to measure electrical resistances, one can still make use of solid contact by embedding a good conductor for heat, e.g. a copper or silver rod into the paramagnetic salt at one end and attaching the specimen to the other end.[24] In all these arrangements one must bear in mind that the heat conductivities of the paramagnetic salts and even of pure metals become very low at these temperatures and that the contact heat resistances are by no means negligible.

The use of liquid helium as a heat transmitting agent may seem at first sight very promising, but there are two main difficulties. The one is that although liquid helium is a 'superconductor' for heat between the λ-point and about 1° K, its thermal conductivity diminishes rapidly so that at very low temperatures thin layers of liquid helium of large areas would be required for satisfactory heat transfer.

The other difficulty of a more general nature is due to the liquid helium film which, as you will hear in Professor ALLEN's lecture, creeps up the wall of the tube connecting the vessel cooled by adiabatic demagnetization and the warmer parts of the apparatus, and, by evaporation and recondensation, causes an appreciable heat influx to the specimen. This difficulty has been overcome by the use of the so-called 'high pressure capsule', which dispenses with connecting tubes. As an example, Fig. 15 shows the arrangement that was used for measuring the

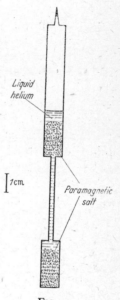

FIG. 15.
Measurement of heat conductivity of liquid helium below 1°K.

heat conductivity of liquid helium below 1° K.[25] The two small metal vessels, connected by a thin-walled tube, each contain some paramagnetic salt; this assembly is filled, at room temperature, with helium to a pressure of about 150 atmospheres and then sealed off. At low temperature the helium condenses, and with appropriate dimensions one can get the whole of the bottom container, the connecting tube and part of the upper container filled with liquid. This capsule is then suspended inside the cryostat exactly in the same way as a paramagnetic salt specimen, and thus its thermal insulation .can be made equally good. The heat conductivity is calculated from the rate at which a small initial temperature difference between the top and bottom container vanishes. These experiments have shown that at low temperatures liquid helium becomes a very poor conductor of heat, and, for instance, at $0 \cdot 1°$ K its conductivity is about one hundredth of that of glass at ordinary temperature.

The sealed capsule arrangement has found many applications, but more recently successful use was also made of a method for cooling helium in an 'open' container[26] as distinct from a sealed capsule. With the help of these various techniques many properties of liquid helium such as specific heat,[22, 27] velocity of second sound,[28] film transfer rate,[29] λ-points of He^3–He^4 mixtures,[30] have been determined down to about $0 \cdot 1°$ K.

Before leaving the subject of heat transfer, there is one other point I want to mention. As we have seen earlier, all entropy and temperature changes connected with magnetic cooling occur in the system composed of the magnetic dipoles, and as the entropy of the lattice is usually negligible, it is immaterial whether the temperature of the lattice follows that of the dipoles. If, however, one wants to cool down other substances this can only be done through the thermal vibrations, and it is essential that the temperature of the dipole system should be communicated rapidly to the lattice. Early theoretical predictions of astronomical equilibrium times fortunately turned out to be over-pessimistic, and it now appears that the time-constant of this process, the so-called spin-lattice relaxation time[31] is even at a few hundredths of a degree well below the time constants of the ordinary heat conduction processes which at these temperatures are measured in seconds or minutes.

Nuclear Paramagnetism

The last topic I want to deal with, namely nuclear para-magnetism, is one that is only just being developed, but is likely to be a fruitful field for the application of these very low temperatures. As briefly mentioned by Professor SIMON, the magnetic moments of nuclei are about 1,000 times smaller than the electronic moments, and to produce entropy changes comparable with those in ordinary para-magnetics about 1,000 times larger values of H/T are required. Nuclear magnetic effects have, of course, been extensively investigated, even at ordinary temperatures, by the nuclear resonance methods,[32] but for bulk-effects temperatures of the order of $1/100°$ K are necessary even with highest magnetic fields at present practicable. Experiments on nuclear paramagnetism at these temperatures can be divided roughly into two categories: those concerned with the purely magnetic and thermal properties of assemblies of nuclei in various substances, and those in which directional effects in other nuclear phenomena, such as radioactive emission, or absorption and scattering of neutrons, are observed on oriented nuclei.

(a) Nuclear Demagnetization

Turning to the first group, adiabatic demagnetization of a nuclear paramagnetic is perhaps the most interesting subject, and it is a measure of the difficulties inherent in this experiment that, although many laboratories have been planning to carry it out, it has not yet been done. Besides the possibility of reaching temperatures of $1/10000°$ or $1/100000°$ K[33] nuclear demagnetization would also give information about the nature of the ordering process in assemblies of nuclei and, in particular, whether at extremely low temperatures some metals would show nuclear ferro-magnetism—a possibility suggested by theory.[34]

For nuclear demagnetization, the nuclear paramagnetic has first of all to be cooled to about $1/100°$ K by thermal contact with an ordinary electron paramagnetic cooling stage. It is next magnetized in 50–100 Kgauss, the heat of magnetization being absorbed by the electronic stage

E

(alternatively the nuclear stage may be cooled to 1/100° K with the magnetic field on), and finally, after thermal contact with the electronic stage has been broken, it is demagnetized. The main, novel, difficulty is the provision of a make-and-brake thermal contact at 1/100° K, and various methods have been proposed.

The superconducting thermal switch offers perhaps the most promising and elegant solution of this problem.[35] The thermal conductivity of superconducting metals is

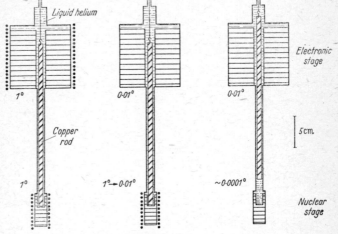

FIG. 16.

Suggested thermal switch using a mobile copper or silver rod as conductor with liquid helium as a heat transmitting 'lubricant'.

very small and diminishes rapidly with temperature, but if the superconductivity is destroyed by a magnetic field, the thermal conductivity increases to the same value as in normal metals. The ratio of the heat conductivities of superconducting to normal metal diminishes roughly proportionally to T^2; this thermal switch therefore becomes more effective as the temperature is lowered, and its suitability has been proved in recent two-stage demagnetization experiments using electron-paramagnetism in both stages.[36]

Another suggested thermal switch uses a mobile copper or silver rod as conductor with liquid helium as a heat transmitting 'lubricant'.[37] Fig. 16 shows the proposed arrangement during the various phases of the experiment, and I will use it, together with Fig. 17, to give some more concrete ideas about nuclear demagnetizations. Of the two vessels shown in Fig. 16 the upper is the electronic stage containing some 250 cc of a paramagnetic salt such as iron ammonium alum, while the lower, small vessel filled with about 10 cc of a suitable nuclear paramagnetic (e.g. copper), is the nuclear stage. The two containers are connected by a tube of about 10 mm diameter and the whole assembly is

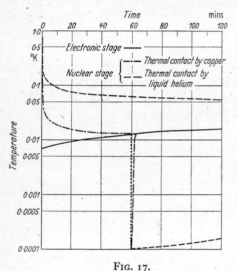

FIG. 17.
Cooling and warming in a proposed nuclear demagnetization experiment.

filled with liquid helium. I have omitted the bath of liquid helium boiling at 1° K and all the other thermal shields, but have indicated the two magnetizing coils type which could provide a field of about 40 Kgauss for the electronic stage and about 60 Kgauss for the narrower nuclear stage.

Initially the whole assembly is magnetized at 1° K; the electronic stage is then demagnetized, and reaches immediately about 0·01° K, while the nuclear stage which remains in the magnetic field, has to be cooled to this temperature through conduction along the connecting tube. If the tube were simply filled with liquid helium which is

a poor heat conductor at these temperatures it would take
excessively long for equilibrium to be established as may
be seen from Fig. 17. If, however, as shown in Fig. 16, a
thick copper rod is placed into this connecting tube,
temperature equilibrium should be established in about one
hour, and the nuclear stage could then be demagnetized
and might cool to, say, 0·0001° K. If the copper rod were
left in the same position, the heat contact between the two-
stages would be still good enough for the nuclear stage to
warm up to the temperature of the electronic stage in a
matter of a few minutes. If, however, by raising the copper
rod one interposed a few centimetres long column of liquid
helium between the end of the rod and the nuclear stage,
the thermal contact between the two stages would be effectively broken, so that the warming-up rate of the nuclear
stage would be determined by the heat leak. The curve in
Fig. 17 is calculated with a heat leak of 1 erg/min. The
trend of the temperature of the electronic stage is also
indicated in Fig. 17; it shows a slow but steady rise caused
by the rather high heat-influx of about 500 ergs/min,
difficult to avoid in such an 'open' helium vessel arrangement.

As you see, one of the main difficulties standing in the
way of successful nuclear cooling is the sluggish heat
transfer at these temperatures. The position may even be
worse than that just described on account of the time-lag
in the energy transfer from nuclear spin to lattice. This
relaxation time is considerably longer than for electron
spins, and it may well be that the use of dielectric crystals
will have to be ruled out on this ground, and one will probably have to rely on metals, with their shorter relaxation
times, for nuclear demagnetization.

(b) Nuclear Orientation and Nuclear Reactions

Ever since the orientation of nuclei on a macroscopic scale
was first envisaged, the possibility of observing directional
effects in nuclear reactions, such as the anisotropy of
radiations from oriented nuclei, was uppermost in every-
one's mind. These experiments may be divided in two

groups. For the first, which comprises, for example, the dependence of the cross-section of nuclei for polarized neutrons as a function of the relative orientation, it is essential that the nuclei should be 'polarized', i.e. should give rise to a net magnetic moment of the specimen. For the other category, only the 'alignment' of the nuclear moments along an axis is of importance, and not the way in which they point; this is the case with the angular distribution of radiations from nuclei which is symmetrical with respect to the equatorial plane of the dipole.

The most direct and general method for producing nuclear '*polarization*' is by application of a strong field (50–100 Kgauss) at low temperature (0·01° K),[33] and we have seen the difficulties that this involves. Another method, proposed by GORTER[38] and by ROSE,[39] which is less general than the 'external field method', but experimentally simpler, does away with the large external field and replaces it, as it were, by the internal magnetic field of several hundred Kgauss due to the electronic moment inside paramagnetic ions. At low temperatures (say about 0·01° K) the nuclear moments will set themselves parallel to this field, so that if the electronic moments are also oriented, which at these temperatures can be achieved by a few hundred oersteds, appreciable nuclear polarization should result.

For nuclear '*alignment*' it has been proposed to use the anisotropic properties of some suitable crystals in which at sufficiently low temperatures the nuclear moments are set along a crystal axis without net polarization. In the method suggested by POUND[40] this is brought about by the interaction of the nuclear electric quadrupole moments with the local electric field, while in the method put forward by BLEANEY[41] which, similarly to the GORTER-ROSE method relies on paramagnetic substances, the electronic moment acts as intermediary for the alignment of the nuclei with respect to a crystal axis.

The first successful experiment on nuclear alignment was carried out in Oxford in September 1951 with the BLEANEY-method.[42] A magnetically dilute single crystal of a Cobalt Tutton salt—the exact composition was (1 % Co, 12 % Cu, 87 % Zn) Rb_2, $(SO_4)_2$, $6H_2O$—containing some radioactive ^{60}Co was cooled by adiabatic demagnetization to about $0.01°$ K, and it was found that, as predicted by theory, the γ-ray intensity perpendicular to the axis of alignment was nearly 50 % higher than parallel to it. Besides demonstrating the existence of the effect, the experiment also furnished the value of the nuclear magnetic moment of a radioactive nucleus, ^{60}Co.[43]

This alignment effect has later also been confirmed in Leiden,[44] and it is to be expected that as the feasibility of this sort of experiments has now been proved, there will ensue a fruitful co-operation between the two disciplines on the opposite extremes of the energy scale, namely low temperature physics and nuclear physics.

I have now come to the end of my survey of temperatures below $1°$ K, and I hope I have justified the privileged position allotted to this particular temperature region. I also hope that this lecture will have helped to convince you that work in this temperature region is full of varied and absorbing interest, and that there is more to it than a mere urge to win a Quixotic race to the unattainable absolute zero.

REFERENCES
General

CASIMIR, H. G. B.; 'Magnetism and Very Low Temperatures', Cambridge, 1940.

VAN VLECK, J. H.; Quelques aspects de la théorie du magnétisme. Annales de l'Institut Henri Poincaré, Vol. 10, 57, 1947.
(A survey of the theory of magnetism with many references to the magnetic cooling method.)

Brief treatments of this subject may also be found in a number of textbooks: e.g. ROBERTS: 'Heat and Thermodynamics', ZEMANSKY: 'Heat and Thermodynamics'.

Text references

[1] KEESOM, W. H.; Leiden Comm. No. 219a (1932).
[2] MENDELSSOHN, K., and MOORE, J. R.; Nature, **133**, 413 (1934). MENDELSSOHN, K., DAUNT, J. G., and PONTIUS, R. B.; 7th Inst. Cong. Refrig. **1**, 445 (1937).
[3] WOLTJER, H. R., and KAMERLINGH ONNES, H.; Leiden Comm. No. 167ᶜ (1923).
[4] DEBYE, P.; Ann. d. Phys., **81**, 1154 (1926).
[5] GIAUQUE, W. F.; J. Am. Chem. Soc., **49**, 1870 (1927).

[6] GIAUQUE, W. F., and MacDOUGALL, D. P.; Phys. Rev., **43**, 768 (1933).
[7] DE HAAS, W. J., WIERSMA, E. C., and KRAMERS, H. A.; Nature, **131**, 719 (1933).
[8] BLAISSE, B. S., COOKE, A. H., and HULL, R. A.; Physica **6**, 219 (1939); COOKE, A. H., and HULL, R. A., Nature, **143**, 799 (1939).
[9] COTTON, A.; Revue Générale de l'Electricitê, Vol. **41**, pp. 3–9 and 131–138 (1937).
[10] KURTI, N., LAINÉ, P., ROLLIN, B. V., and SIMON, F.; C. R. Acad. Sci. **202**, 1421, (1936).
[11] BITTER, F.; Rev. Sci. Inst., **7**, 479 and 483 (1936).
[12] TSAI, B.; Physical Society Cambridge Conference Report, p. 72 (1947).
[13] e.g. COOKE, A. H.; Proc. Phys. Soc., A. **62**, 269 (1949).
[14] e.g. DE KLERK, D., STEENLAND, M. J., and GORTER, C. J.; Physica, **15**, 649 (1949).
[15] e.g. GIAUQUE, W. F., and MacDOUGALL, D. P.; J. Am. Chem. Soc., **60**. 376 (1938).
[16] e.g. BAGGULEY, D. M. S., BLEANEY, B., GRIFFITHS, J. H. E., PENROSE, R. P., and PLUMPTON, B. I.; Proc. Phys. Soc., A. **61**, 542, 551 (1948).
[17] DE KLERK, D., STEENLAND, M. J., and GORTER, C. J.; Physica, **16**, 571 (1950).
[18] KURTI, N., LAINÉ, P., and SIMON, F.; C. R. Acad. Sc. **204**, 675 (1937).
[19] KURTI, N.; Journ. de Physique, **12**, 281 (1951).
[20] GARRETT, C. G. B.; J. Chem. Phys., **19**, 1154 (1951). ZIMAN, J. M.; Proc. Phys. Soc., A. **64**, 1108 (1951).
[21] COOKE, A. H., and HULL, R. A.; Proc. Roy. Soc. A, **181**, 83 (1942).
[22] HULL, R. A., WILKINSON, K. R., and WILKS, J.; Proc. Phys. Soc., A. **64**, 364 (1951).
[23] KURTI, N., and SIMON, F.; Proc. Roy. Soc., A. **151**, 610 (1935).
[24] MENDOZA, E.; Les Phénomènes Cryomagnétiques (Paris: Cérémonies Langevin-Perrin), p. 53 (1948).
[25] KURTI, N., and SIMON, F.; Nature, **142**, 207 (1938).
[26] HUDSON, R. P., HUNT, D., and KURTI, N.; Proc. Phys. Soc., A. **62**, 392(1949).
[27] KRAMERS, H. C.; Proc. Oxford Conference on Low Temperature Physics (1951), p. 93.
[28] ATKINS, K. R., and OSBORNE, D. V.; Phil. Mag., **41**, 1078 (1950).
[29] AMBLER, E., and KURTI, N.; Phil. Mag., **43**, 260 (1952).
[30] DAUNT, J. G., and HEER, C. V.; Phys. Rev., **78**, 342 (1950).
[31] e.g. COOKE, A. H.; Rep. on Progress in Physics, **13**, 276 (1950).
[32] e.g. ROLLIN, B. V.; Rep. on Progress in Physics, **12**, 22 (1949).
[33] GORTER, C. J.; Phys. Z., **35**, 923, 1934. KURTI, N., and SIMON, F.; Proc. Roy. Soc., A. **149**, 152 (1935). SIMON, F.; C. R. Cong. sur le Magnétisme, Strasbourg, **3**, 1 (1939).
[34] FRÖHLICH, H., and NABARRO, F. R. N.; Proc. Roy. Soc., A. **175**, 382 (1940).
[35] DAUNT, J. G., and HEER, C. V.; Phys. Rev., **76**, 985 (1949).
[36] DARBY, J., HATTON, J., ROLLIN, B. V., SEYMOUR, E. F. W., and SILSBEE, H. S.; Proc. Phys. Soc., A. **64**, 861 (1951).
[37] KURTI, N.; Les Phénomènes Cryomagnétiques (Paris, Cérémonies Langevin-Perrin), p. 29 (1948).
[38] GORTER, C. J.; Physica, **14**, 504 (1948).
[39] ROSE, M. E.; Phys. Rev., **75**, 213 (1949).
[40] POUND, R. V.; Phys. Rev., **76**, 1410 (1949).
[41] BLEANEY, B.; Proc. Phys. Soc., A. **64**, 315 (1951); Phil. Mag., **42**, 441 (1951).
[42] DANIELS, J. M., GRACE, M. A., and ROBINSON, F. N. H.; Nature, **168**, 780 (1951).
[43] BLEANEY, B., DANIELS, J. M., GRACE, M. A., HALBAN, H., KURTI, N., and ROBINSON, F. N. H.; Phys. Rev., **84**, Febr. (1952).
[44] GORTER, C. J., POPPEMA, O. J., STEENLAND, M. J., and BEUN, J. A.; Physica, **17**, 1050 (1951).

LIQUID HELIUM

by J. F. ALLEN

Introduction—Pre-History

HELIUM HAS ALWAYS been a most remarkable and entertaining substance. In the first place, consider the manner of its discovery. Most of the rarer elements have been found by painstaking search and careful chemical isolation, but helium was discovered almost by accident and not, first of all, on the earth but in the sun! In fact, after the first discovery of helium in the solar atmosphere, nearly thirty years were to elapse before it was found to be present on the earth.

The detection of helium in the sun came about in the following way. The solar eclipse in the summer of 1868 was the first eclipse to be studied quantitatively with the aid of accurate instruments, of which the most powerful was the spectroscope. During the period of totality of the eclipse, both Sir NORMAN LOCKYER and the French scientist JANSSEN succeeded in obtaining spectroscopic records of the emission spectra of the solar atmosphere, and both of these scientists reported the presence of a bright yellow line of wavelength 5876 Å close to the sodium D lines. Provisionally called D3, opinions were expressed that the new yellow line was either an emission from hydrogen or a faulty observation of the sodium lines themselves, although LOCKYER was quite convinced that neither of these two substances was responsible for a line in that position in the spectrum.

In 1871, Lord KELVIN announced at the British Association meeting that D3 was not reproduced in any terrestrial flame, and that it must therefore be an emission from some new and unknown substance. LOCKYER for purposes of laboratory convenience gave it the name helium.

A quarter of a century later, in January 1895, Sir WILLIAM RAMSAY, searching for unlikely compounds of argon, boiled some Norwegian cleveite (a uranium ore) with dilute sulphuric acid and collected the evolved gases which were mainly argon. He filled a Geissler tube with the gas and on passing a discharge through it, saw for the first time the D3 line in the laboratory. In August of the same year, KAYSER, again looking for argon in natural well gases, found large traces of helium in the gas from a well in Wildbad in the Black Forest. There was an immediate race to separate the gas in pure form in quantity and to try to liquefy it. With surprising speed OLSZEWSKI in Warsaw made the first attempt at liquefaction in 1896. It was unsuccessful, as were the attempts of DEWAR in 1901, TRAVERS in 1903 and again that of OLSZEWSKI in 1905. It was left to the more patient and methodical KAMERLINGH ONNES to observe for the first time in July 1908 liquid helium boiling quietly in a Dewar flask. He estimated the normal boiling point to be in the neighbourhood of $4°$ K and on the same day, by reducing the vapour pressure over the boiling liquid, he succeeded in reaching a temperature of about $1°$ K in a vain attempt to produce solid helium.

Equilibrium Properties of the Liquid

Before describing the properties of the liquid we must say a few words about the fundamental nature of the substance helium itself. Normal atmospheric or well helium consists of a mixture of the two isotopes ^4_2He and ^3_2He, in relative concentrations of about 10^6 to 1. The rare isotope ^3He was discovered by ASTON in 1920. One can get enriched mixtures of ^3He in ^4He by performing various operations on liquid helium, but pure ^3He must be 'grown' in a nuclear reactor and something like a litre of the pure gas has now been produced by this means. Although the complete process has not been disclosed, the lithium-neutron reaction is a likely one. Lithium bombarded with neutrons yields ^4He and tritium ^3_1H. The latter can be separated from the mixture by passing it through a palladium valve. Tritium is unstable and suffers beta-decay with a half life of twelve years, the resulting product being ^3_2He, which can be collected periodically by solidifying the tritium.

In speaking of liquid helium we are therefore concerned with two liquids, since ^{3}He has now been successfully lique-fied (SYDORIAK, GRILLY and HAMMEL[1]).

Some of the critical data of the two liquids are given for comparison in Table I and depicted in Fig. 1.

TABLE I

	Liquid $^4_2$He	Liquid $^3_2$He
Critical temperature..	5.2°K	3.3°K
Normal boiling point..	4.2°K	3.2°K
Maximum density under s.v.p. ..	0.145 gm per cm³	0.08 gm per cm³
Maximum heat of vaporization ..	93 joules per mole	59 joules per mole
Maximum surface tension	1.3 dynes per cm	?
Index of refraction	1.02	?

Liquid ^{3}He is a fascinating new liquid and it will be extremely interesting to observe it and measure its proper-ties in more detail, but we are more concerned here with liquid ^{4}He, which we shall call simply liquid helium, and when we speak of liquid ^{3}He it will be referred to as such.

Perhaps the most striking thing about the appearance of liquid helium is that it is nearly always very difficult to see! It is colourless, and with its feeble surface tension and gas-like index of refraction there is not much of a meniscus and a negligible lens effect in curved vessels. Also, unless it is well protected from conducted and radiated heat it quickly evaporates because of its extremely small heat of vaporiza-tion and low density. Normally it is collected in silvered glass Dewar vessels which have a clear viewing strip down either side. It is given further protection from radiant heat by surrounding the helium Dewar with another containing either liquid hydrogen or liquid nitrogen. In vessels en-tirely surrounded with liquid hydrogen the evaporation rate can be reduced to the order of 1 cm³ per hour which

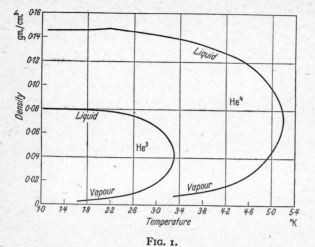

FIG. 1.

Liquid and vapour density curves of He⁴ and He³.
Plotted according to the law of rectilinear diameters.

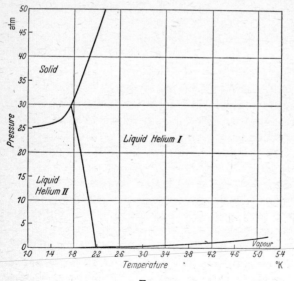

FIG. 2.

Phase diagram of liquid helium.

means that experiments with liquid helium can last for many hours. Normally, experiments are carried out with anything from 10 cm^3 to 500 cm^3 of liquid in the Dewar vessel.

If we look at the phase diagram of helium, which is shown in Fig. 2, we see the first of the many strange properties of the liquid. Normal substances have a 'triple point', that is a pressure and temperature at which solid, liquid and vapour are present and in equilibrium with each other. That is not the case with helium, which has no triple point. In helium the liquid phase extends right down to the absolute zero and one must apply a pressure of 25 atmospheres or more to the liquid in order to solidify it. One can also solidify it at higher temperatures by compressing the gas, and in this way solid helium has recently been produced at 50° K by subjecting the gas to a pressure of 7000 atmospheres. This experiment was performed by SIMON and his collaborators and was described in Prof. SIMON's lecture.

The shape of the melting curve of helium at the lowest temperature is very interesting because it points to an important property of the liquid. We can write the CLAUSIUS-CLAPEYRON equation in the form $\dfrac{dp}{dT} = \dfrac{\Delta S}{\Delta V}$. The left hand side of this equation here represents the slope of the melting curve and experiment indicates that this slope approaches zero as the temperature approaches zero. Therefore the expression on the right hand side of the equation must likewise approach zero. Hence, since ΔV, the change of volume on melting, remains finite then ΔS, the change of entropy on melting, must vanish as T approaches zero. This is in accordance with the third law of thermodynamics, and we are thus faced with the fact that the liquid at the absolute zero must be in a highly ordered state. Now liquid helium is a highly mobile liquid with negligible viscosity so that we cannot expect it to show the same *kind* of highly ordered state as a crystalline solid, but it *must* attain some state of perfect order so that its entropy can approach zero at the absolute zero. The precise nature of this ordered state is the crucial problem of liquid helium and it is still very imperfectly understood.

We mentioned earlier that the density of liquid helium was 0·145 gm per cm³. If we take the reciprocal of that and use molar quantities, we find that the specific volume of the liquid is approximately 27 cm³ per mole. Now the helium atom has a gas kinetic diameter of something like 2·7 × 10⁻⁸ cm. If we close-pack spheres of this diameter, the resulting specific volume would be about 8 cm³ per mole. In normal liquids, such calculated and observed specific volumes agree fairly well, but in liquid helium we see that the values differ by a factor of more than three. SIMON discovered a possible reason for this in 1932. He noticed that helium showed a pronounced departure from TROUTON's Rule, according to which the ratio of the latent heat of vaporization to the normal boiling point, L/T, should for all liquids have a value of about 80 when measured in Joules per mole per °K. Helium showed the only significant departure with a value of 20. SIMON suggested that TROUTON's Rule should be modified so as to embrace the zero point energy, E_0, as well as the energy involved in vaporization, and it ought therefore to be written $\dfrac{L+E_0}{T} \doteqdot 80$, which gives a value $E_0 \doteqdot 240$ joules per mole for helium.

Before we comment on this we must say a few words about the nature of zero point energy. The idea arose originally from the quantum theory which describes the ground state of a linear harmonic oscillator as having an energy $\frac{1}{2}h\nu$. If a particle of mass m is confined in a 'box' by its nearest neighbours at their appropriate mean separation R (calculated from the observed specific volume), then by means of wave mechanics we can calculate the 'zero point energy' which the particle will possess by virtue of its freedom to move within that box. Proceeding in this way, if R^3 is the size of the box and the particle is a helium atom, the zero point energy of liquid helium is $E_0 \sim \dfrac{3}{8}\dfrac{h^2}{m R^2} \doteqdot 200$ joules per mole, which is about right.

In other words, E_0 which here manifests itself as a pressure, is almost as large as the energy which binds the atoms together in the liquid, the net balance being L. On this picture, then, liquid helium is dominated by its zero point energy and as a result it is 'blown-up' to a volume three times as great as it should be. To put it in another way we can say that helium forms a 'quantum' liquid, that is a liquid whose properties are dominated more by quan-

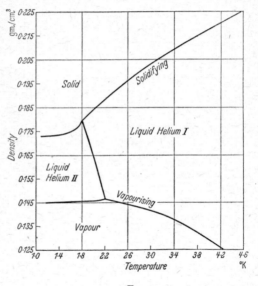

FIG. 3.
Density-temperature diagram of liquid helium.

tum laws than by the laws of classical physics. These considerations also show us why we do not observe solid helium under its saturated vapour pressure, but why we must apply external pressure in order to force the helium atoms sufficiently close together so that they can crystallize.

In practically all other liquids and solids the zero point energy is much smaller than in helium, due to larger values of m, while the binding energies may be some tens of thousands of joules per mole. In liquid ^{3}He, however, with its small m and very low density, zero point energy ought again to play an important rôle, so important in fact, that before 1949, many theoretical physicists were of the opinion that ^{3}He would not be able to liquefy at all under a saturated vapour pressure.

If we return now to the phase diagram of liquid helium, we see that it is crossed by a line which has been called the λ-line, for reasons which will presently emerge. On either side of the line the liquid exists in different modifications. The high temperature form, called helium I, is a more or less normal liquid (always remembering its quantum nature), while the low temperature form, called helium II, has many strange 'superfluid' properties. The possibly unimaginative numerical nomenclature was given by KEE-SOM who first discovered the λ-line a quarter of a century ago.

It was the measurement of the density (Fig. 3) and the dielectric constant of the liquid which first showed the existence of the two modifications. Both of these properties, density and dielectric constant, show a sharp maximum at the boundary temperature, 2·19° K, which means that helium II has a negative expansion coefficient. The maximum in the density curve was actually discovered by ONNES in 1910 but at that time he assumed it to be a phenomenon similar to that in water at 4° C.

It was not until 1930, however, that the really spectacular nature of the transformation at 2·19° K was disclosed. KEESOM and CLUSIUS, measuring the specific heat, observed a very sharp peak at the transformation temperature. This is shown in Fig. 4. The general shape of the curve with its admittedly somewhat sketchy resemblance to the Greek letter λ led EHRENFEST to call the transformation a λ-transition and the temperature of 2·19° K the λ-point.

The type of transition represented by a λ-point is very interesting. The change of phase from solid to liquid or liquid to vapour is characterized by the presence of a latent heat and by discontinuities in the specific volume and specific heat. Such a change is called a first order transition. Second order phase transitions such as λ-points, are characterized by an absence of latent heat but by discontinuities in the specific heat and in the gradient of the specific volume at the transition temperature. The λ-point in liquid helium is the most spectacular of these, but other notable examples are the CURIE points in ferromagnetics and ferro-electrics and the order-disorder transformations in alloys such as β-brass.

Transport Properties

Now the specific heat curve of any substance is very important because it describes how the internal energy of a substance increases its value with rising temperature. The

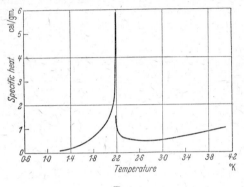

FIG. 4.
Variation of specific heat with temperature.

problem of liquid helium thus becomes one of understanding why the energy goes into the system in such a manner as to cause a λ-shaped specific heat curve. Some of the clues to this problem were discovered through a study of the heat flow and mass flow, that is, the thermal conductivity and viscosity of the liquid.

Here we come to a very interesting and striking phenomenon. Liquid helium I boils violently with clouds of small bubbles while its vapour pressure (and hence its temperature) is being reduced, but on passing the λ-point all boiling abruptly ceases and the liquid becomes clear and quiescent although still evaporating very rapidly. This very pronounced and beautiful phenomenon had been observed in Toronto in 1929 and described in a paper by McLennan, Smith and Wilhelm in 1932. It is strange, however, that it had passed unnoticed for over twenty years, because Onnes first saw liquid helium at 1° K in 1908, and Keesom pointed out in the early 1930's that there was no observable change in the appearance of the liquid as the λ-point was passed.

The absence of boiling in helium II went unexplained until Keesom showed in 1935 that although helium I had a normal thermal conductivity of the order of 10^{-5} watt units, helium II transferred heat a million times as well as that! We now know that in certain circumstances helium II will conduct heat ten thousand times better than will copper. The absence of boiling is thus simply due to the fact that owing to the enormously high heat conductivity it is impossible in a bath of helium II to produce a temperature difference between top and bottom of the liquid sufficiently great to allow the formation of a bubble of vapour. One can in fact pump off the vapour so rapidly that the surface throws up spray an inch or two in height and yet the liquid underneath is completely clear and free of bubbles. An elementary calculation based on the absence of boiling yields a value of thermal conductivity of the bulk liquid at least ten to a hundred times as great as that of copper.

A moment ago we said that 'in certain circumstances' helium II is an exceptionally good conductor of heat. The reason for using such an odd qualifying phrase is this: helium II has a thermal 'conductivity' which depends very sensitively not only on the temperature, but on the temperature gradient and on the geometry of the measuring container as well! The very high conductivity of 10^4 watt units mentioned earlier (that of copper being about 1 watt unit) would be observed in a capillary about 0·25 mm diameter, at a temperature of 1·9° K and along a temperature gradient of 10^{-4} deg. per cm. Dependence on the temperature gradient strictly speaking violates the definition of thermal conductivity and the use of the term in connection with helium II is only justified for descriptive purposes. The

F

temperature variation of thermal 'conductivity', shown in Fig. 5, indicates a rapidly rising value effectively from zero at the λ-point to a maximum in the neighbourhood of $1\cdot9°$ K thereafter falling off with a fairly high power of T towards zero at $0°$ K. Since the maximum shifts to higher temperatures as the gradient diminishes, it seems likely that for a vanishingly small gradient and under certain geometrical conditions the maximum in the conductivity curve is actually at the λ-point.

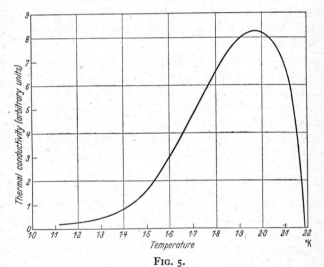

FIG. 5.

Curve showing the general nature of the variation of thermal 'conductivity' of helium II with temperature.

The phenomenon which dominates thermal processes in helium II is the momentum transfer which has been found to accompany heat flow, and which was discovered by ALLEN and JONES in 1938. Both the variability and the very high value of the thermal conductivity can be accounted for in terms of 'forced-convection' currents in the liquid. The momentum transfer is in such a direction that liquid is forced to flow *up* the temperature gradient, thus creating a higher level (and hence higher pressure) in any region where a higher temperature exists. The hydrostatic

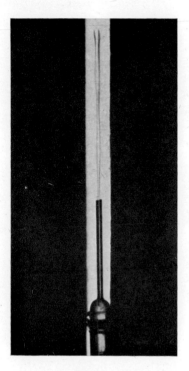

PLATE 1.
The helium II fountain.

pressure which can be produced in this way is very great, being of the order of one atmosphere per degree of temperature difference.

If the apparatus is suitably arranged, say as in Fig. 6, then a highly spectacular demonstration of such momentum transfer may be given. A tube open at both ends has its upper end in the form of a capillary 1 mm or so in diameter. The tube is filled with emery powder held in at the bottom by wire gauze. The tube is suspended in a helium bath at 1° K with its open capillary protruding above the surface.

If a powerful light and heat source (say a 150 watt lamp) is shone on the tube, liquid helium will spurt from the capillary in a jet or fountain which may be a foot or more in height. The radiant heat is absorbed by the black emery powder and is conducted down to the bath, while the liquid helium rushes up the temperature gradient to produce the jet. Plate I shows such a jet.

It was an experiment of this kind that led to the name 'fountain effect' being given to the phenomenon. Such a device forms a very simple and highly efficient heat engine and, moreover, one that is reversible, since

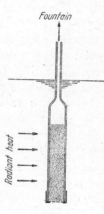

FIG. 6.
Method of demonstration of the helium fountain.

DAUNT and MENDELSSOHN were able to show that a temperature difference existed between the ends of a powder-filled tube through which helium II was flowing.

Ordinary convection plays no part in the fountain phenomenon, and to explain it—that is to explain the momentum transfer associated with heat flow—we must allow the liquid to be endowed with a very peculiar structure. It would appear that the liquid forms a system with more than one component; in other words there must be some *fraction* of the liquid which is forced *up* the temperature gradient and which either leaves the remaining fraction behind or which forces it back *down* the gradient to provide the heat-carrying convection currents. This concept, which imagines the liquid to be composed of two 'separate' fluids, having different properties, but present simultaneously in intimate mixture is called the two-fluid hypothesis, and it has been the basis of most of the theoretical speculation on liquid helium for the past dozen years.

Something of the nature of the two 'fluids' became clear through a study of the properties of flow of helium II, although the clarification was preceded by a good deal of confusion. Various experiments were performed in Cambridge, Toronto, Leiden and Moscow and in each case different results and conflicting values of the viscosity coefficient were obtained. It seemed as if the value depended not only on the type of experiment but also on the place where the experiment had been performed; a state of affairs which is scientifically undesirable.

There were three principal types of experiment. In Leiden observations were made on the damping of a disc oscillating in its own plane in the helium bath. In Cambridge and Toronto flow was observed through capillary tubes, while in Moscow KAPITZA allowed the flow to take place radially through a narrow flat annular gap. The oscillating disc and the POISEUILLE flow methods both gave the same results in helium I, a low gas-type viscosity (of the order of 10^{-5} poise) in which the coefficient declined with falling temperature. In helium II the disc showed a coefficient which declined with a high power of the temperature, but the capillary flow measurements were quite different. Close to the λ-point and in short fat capillaries a more or less true viscosity was observed, but it was very difficult to produce non-turbulent flow.

It was in capillaries of half a millimetre or less in diameter that strange things happened. The rate of flow depended less and less on the hydrostatic pressure and on the length of the capillary as the diameter of the capillary was reduced. To produce channels smaller than 0·1 mm another technique was used. A metal tube several millimetres in diameter was filled with several thousand small copper wires laid parallel to each other. The tube was then drawn down so that the wires were squeezed into a close-packed hexagonal mass. Channels always appeared to remain, however, between the hexagonal flat adjacent surfaces of the wires, channels which were sometimes less than a wavelength of light in width. Helium II flowed readily through such narrow channels although they proved completely impervious to helium I. In such narrow channels 10^{-3} to 10^{-5} cm in width the rate of flow of helium II was strictly independent of pressure and, strangest of all, the velocity of flow appeared to be roughly *inversely* proportional to the width of the channels, in other words, the narrower the channel the faster the flow of helium II! The temperature variation of such flow through very narrow channels is represented in Fig. 7 where the measurements extend from the λ-point down to about $1°$ K. No flow measurements have yet been made below the latter temperature. Flow through a wide tube filled with tightly packed jeweller's rouge (giving tortuous channels of 10^{-5} cm or less in width) showed a similar temperature variation, but showed, surprisingly, a definite dependence of velocity on pressure such that close to the λ-point $v \propto p$ while at lower temperatures $v \propto p^{\frac{1}{2}}$ fairly accurately. Finally, KAPITZA'S method of radial flow between closely lapped annuli yielded again $v \propto p^{\frac{1}{2}}$ and from the geometry of his apparatus he deduced an upper limit to the coefficient of viscosity of helium II of 10^{-11} poise.

Now, since most of these experiments appeared to have a certain degree of veracity about them, the nature of liquid helium must be such as to fit each separate result. The problem is somewhat reminiscent of the blind men and the elephant.

The Mobile Film

But while the viscosity controversy continued, a new property of the liquid emerged, that of the mobile film. As far back as 1915 ONNES had recorded that all vessels partially immersed in a liquid helium bath at $1°$ K filled themselves to the same level as the bath—a species of hydrostatic paradox but without any obvious connecting liquid channels. ROLLIN and SIMON were the first to suggest the possibility of liquid transfer by a mobile film but it was left to DAUNT and MENDELSSOHN to prove the existence of the film and to measure its principal properties. In a series of elegant experiments they showed that, (a) helium II creeps in the form of a film over all solid surfaces above the bath level, so long as the temperature of those surfaces is below the λ-point; (b) the transfer is in such a direction as to produce the same level in all vessels at the same temperature; (c) the transfer in the film is frictionless, or nearly so, since the rate of transfer is, to a first approximation, independent of the length of path which it must traverse; (d) the rate of transfer is zero at the λ-point and that it rises steadily towards a maximum, in the neighbourhood of 8×10^{-5} cm³ per second per cm width of path, at the lowest temperatures. The temperature variation is approximately represented by the curve in Fig. 7; (e) the film will flow up a temperature gradient so that the liquid level will stand higher in the vessel at the higher temperature; in other words, the fountain effect operates in films as well as in the bulk liquid; (f) the film conducts heat to a negligible degree; and (g) the film is about 3×10^{-6} cm (that is of the order of 100 atoms) thick.

One of the DAUNT and MENDELSSOHN experiments was quite dramatic. A small glass beaker was filled with helium II and then lifted clear of the bath. Liquid helium, creeping over the lip of the beaker as a film, collected on the bottom surface and dripped off as though the beaker were leaking.

If we add all of this to the apparently confused results of the viscosity measurements, the following picture emerges. As we said before, for purposes of description of most of the properties of helium II, we can consider the liquid to be composed of an intimate mixture of two fluids, the relative proportions of which are a function of the temperature. One of these fluids is called the superfluid of density ρ_s, and of zero or vanishingly small viscosity, and the other is the normal fluid of density ρ_n. If ρ is the measured density of the liquid helium II, then

$$\rho = \rho_n + \rho_s$$

and the variation is such that at the absolute zero $\rho_s/\rho = 1$ and at the λ-point $\rho_n/\rho = 1$. For simplicity we shall sometimes refer to the liquids simply by their density symbols.

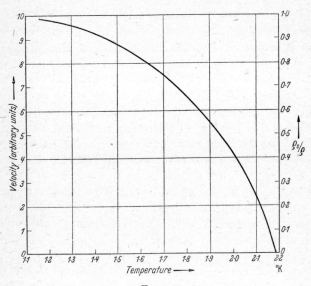

FIG. 7.

Superfluid transfer and superfluid concentration in helium II as a function of temperature.

The graph which is drawn is the smoothed curve of the experimental determination of ρ_s/ρ. The curves showing film transfer, flow through very narrow channels and flow through tightly packed rouge, all lie so closely about the drawn curve that within the experimental error one can probably say they are the same.

It is now clear that in the oscillating disc method of measuring viscosity in helium II the disc is acted upon principally by the normal fluid, which possesses a real viscosity, the superfluid fraction sliding freely over it. At any rate, it can be said to slide freely over it if the peripheral velocity of the disc is small. At greater peripheral velocities the picture is not quite so clear. In flow through large tubes the normal fluid is also dominant so that one measures a real viscosity, while as the tube gets smaller, the normal fluid is held back and the superfluid, which does not exchange momentum with the wall, slips through. In the very narrowest channels of all, whose widths are similar to the film thickness, the flow closely resembles that of the mobile film in magnitude and temperature dependence. This can be seen in Fig. 7.

ANDRONIKASHVILI[2] has recently measured the viscosity of the normal fluid by the oscillating disc method originally used in 1936 by MacWood in Leiden. MacWood had assumed the whole liquid was concerned because in those days there were no such things as ρ_n and ρ_s. ANDRONIKASHVILI corrected MacWood's results by using appropriate values for ρ_n and extended the measurements to $1\cdot2°$ K. He found that the viscosity of the normal fluid, as shown in Fig. 8, first declines with temperature and then after a bit rises steeply again at the lowest temperatures.

Fig. 8 also shows the variation of viscosity of helium I and here again we see an odd effect. BOWERS and MENDELSSOHN[3] have found that below $3°$ K the viscosity appears to drop off in such a way as to pass smoothly through the λ-point with no discontinuity. It would appear that helium I below $3°$ K 'anticipates' the onset of helium II, but beyond that one can say little at the moment to explain the effect. Although on simple kinetic grounds one might expect the same sort of thing to appear in the thermal conductivity of liquid helium I, this is not the case. The thermal conductivity just above the λ-point gives no indication of the impending super heat transfer of helium II.

The flow measurements throw more light on the mechanism of heat transfer and the momentum transfer which accompanies it in helium II. For reasons which we shall come to presently, it appears that it is the superfluid which flows up a temperature gradient and the normal fluid which flows down. This circulation of the slippery superfluid, which slides freely not only over all surfaces but through the normal fluid, and the normal fluid itself with its own low gas-like viscosity provides the convection current which gives the liquid its extraordinary ability to transfer heat.

The mobile film, on the other hand, is essentially a poor conductor of heat, because although the superfluid in the film can move easily towards the source of heat, no return flow and therefore no convection current is possible since the normal fluid is held immobile on the wall by its viscosity.

The complete picture is actually a little more complicated than this. It was found by KAPITZA[4] and confirmed more recently by OSBORNE[5] that although the bulk liquid might be called a super-conductor of heat, the actual transfer of

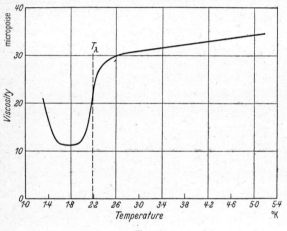

FIG. 8.

Variation of coefficient of viscosity with temperature.
Helium I: (after BOWERS and MENDELSSOHN[3]).
Helium II: (after ANDRONIKASHVILI[2]). The curve represents the viscosity of the 'normal' fluid only.

heat from any solid surface into the liquid takes place very inefficiently. It is as if all surfaces immersed in the liquid were covered by a very thin, poorly-conducting boundary layer. This may presumably be explained in the following way. Since the superfluid has apparently no viscosity, it does not readily exchange momentum with the wall of the vessel and therefore does not readily exchange energy with it, which it presumably must do if heat is to be imparted to the liquid. The superfluid thus behaves as though it had a very low accommodation coefficient.

The Two-Fluid Theory

We must now begin to contemplate some of the theoretical ideas concerning the nature of liquid helium. The first of these, by F. LONDON and TISZA, arose from the fact that the helium atom possesses a symmetrical wave function and should therefore in the gas state obey BOSE–EINSTEIN statistics. LONDON pointed out that the onset of the degenerate state of such an assembly is marked by a critical temperature and a specific heat anomaly in which the temperature gradient of the specific heat shows a discontinuity. Below the critical temperature the atoms begin to 'condense' into the ground state from the excited energy levels and in an ideal gas composed of weakly interacting helium atoms that critical temperature would be in the neighbourhood of $3°$ K. Of course the real gas has become a liquid at such a temperature and it becomes an important matter to decide whether the much stronger interaction between the atoms in the liquid state will smear out the specific heat anomaly or accentuate it into the sharp peak observed at the λ-point in liquid helium. We shall come back to this matter a little later.

Meanwhile, the BOSE–EINSTEIN condensation phenomenon together with the observation of frictionless superfluid flow led TISZA to the idea that the 'condensed' fraction of helium atoms might correspond to the superfluid part of helium II. If so, then for low values of the momentum the superfluid might be expected to have a very long mean free path and hence could pass freely through the normal liquid or over surfaces. Furthermore, and this is the crux of the matter, the superfluid would carry no entropy with it, and therefore could be considered to be effectively at the absolute zero.

Following these ideas H. LONDON presented a thermodynamical theory of the fountain phenomenon based on an analogy with the thermoelectric effect and which yielded the fountain pressure in terms of the entropy defect of the flowing superfluid,

$$\frac{dp}{dT} = \rho S$$

where p is the fountain pressure, and S is the specific entropy of He II. This relation has been abundantly proved by several experimenters, notably by KAPITZA[6] and MELLINK[7]. From such experiments KAPITZA was able to give ρ_n as a function of temperature and to show that the super-fluid fraction carried effectively zero entropy. KAPITZA suspended an insulated vessel in a helium II bath in such a way that the only entry to it was by means of superfluid flow through a very narrow channel. He measured the rate of flow into the vessel when the inside was supplied with just sufficient heat to maintain zero temperature difference between vessel and bath. He found that the heat supplied was equal to the total enthalpy of the helium that entered, thus showing that the superfluid on entering the vessel was effectively at absolute zero. The mechano-caloric or reverse fountain effect now becomes clear. If helium is allowed to flow through a porous plug only the ρ_s can get through and ρ_n, which carries all of the heat content or enthalpy, is left behind thus causing the temperature of the held-back liquid to rise. The heat is strained out, so to speak.

Another particularly neat experiment by ANDRONIKASH-VILI[8] demonstrated the temperature variation of ρ_n in the following way. A torsion fibre suspended a pile of fairly closely packed discs, the gaps between them being of the order of $0 \cdot 1$ mm. From the oscillation of the pile of discs the moment of inertia of the assembly could be calculated. Now the separation of the discs was so small that of the liquid between them, the fraction ρ_n was carried completely, effectively 'locked' to the discs by viscosity, while the fraction ρ_s was not moved at all since it could slip freely. Thus, when the pile of discs oscillated at the λ-point, all of the contained liquid rotated, while at $1°$ K where ρ_n was not more than 3 per cent of ρ the discs carried practically no liquid with them. Hence the observed moment of inertia of the system varied with temperature. The resulting determination of ρ_n as a function of temperature agreed well with the determinations by KAPITZA and others.

From the various determinations of ρ_n one can calculate the variation of ρ_s with temperature and this is shown in

Fig. 7. The similarity between ρ_s/ρ, film transfer, and flow through narrow straight channels and tortuous channels (jeweller's rouge) is so great that one curve suffices for all four properties, the individual departures being not greater than about 5 per cent and these are probably due to experimental error.

The close similarity of the phenomena illustrated in Fig. 7 now permits us to draw a clearer picture of the transport properties of helium II when the flow is through very narrow channels or by means of film transfer, in other words, a clearer picture of superfluid flow. First of all, as we said before, we imagine the liquid both in narrow channels and in the film to have the correct proportions of ρ_n and ρ_s in equilibrium with the local temperature, because only at the absolute zero could the liquid or film be entirely composed of superfluid. But the normal fluid in either the channel or the film is held immobile by its viscosity so that when flow or film transfer takes place only the superfluid can move since it does not exchange momentum either with the wall or, to a first approximation at any rate, with the normal fluid. Consequently, the liquid which is transferred is more or less 'pure' superfluid and any energy changes in film or channel take place at either end.

The pressure in a bath of helium II can now be given by

$$P = \rho\,g\,h + \rho\,S\,\varDelta\,T$$

where the first term on the right hand side represents the normal hydrostatic pressure and the second term represents the thermo-mechanical or fountain pressure due to the temperature difference $\varDelta T$. If two reservoirs are connected either by a boundary wall or by a capillary tube, then flow will take place either by film transfer over the wall or by superflow through the capillary tube until the pressure equation is satisfied. If, for example, the two connected vessels are at the same temperature then the transfer will proceed to equalize the levels.

What is perhaps not so clearly understood is the precise *kinetic* process by which superfluid transfer is instituted and maintained, although descriptions have been attempted in terms of osmotic pressure or zero-point 'diffusion'. It seems, however, to be quite clear that the film transfer does not proceed in the manner of a siphon. DAUNT and MENDELSSOHN[9] have shown that the 'characteristic' transfer rate at $1°$ K of about 30 cm per sec. can be produced by a level difference ten times as small as that which would be required to give such a velocity under a free fall.

Again, at first sight, it seems energetically untidy to have a film transfer 'velocity' which increases as the temperature falls, but if the transfer rate is linked with the concentration of ρ_s, as would appear from Fig. 7, then the untidiness disappears, for then one can impute a constant 'velocity' to the superfluid fraction. Of course this leaves one with the need to explain why this velocity should be about 30 cm per sec. which is again difficult. At $1°$ K, where ρ_n is only about 3 per cent of the whole, the transfer velocity is the velocity of practically the whole film, and therefore, represents the 'streaming' velocity of the superfluid in the film, if one uses a not too close analogy with a KNUDSEN gas. But it must be remembered that this 'streaming' velocity of 30 cm per sec. bears no relation to the zero point velocity of a helium atom in the liquid which is of the order of 10^4 cm per sec. Presumably the streaming velocity corresponds to the upper limit of momentum beyond which exchange takes place with the wall. Such a condition might be expected to give rise to a velocity independent of the length of film path or narrow channel and this, to a first approximation, is what is observed.

Film Theories

Having described the motion of the film it is now somewhat easier to see how the film comes into existence in the first place, but what is again difficult is to explain why it should be several hundred atoms thick. Although theories here have not been entirely successful, they have served the useful purpose of stimulating experiments to measure the film profile. It is obvious that such a mobile film is not likely to be of uniform thickness, for at any point on its surface an atom will be in equilibrium between the attractive force to the wall and the gravitational force, and the film will therefore tend to thicken at the base.

BIJL, MICHELS and DE BOER[10] considered the film to be 'blown-up' by an additional zero point energy arising from an uncertainty in length equal to the film thickness, d. This theory yielded $d \propto H^{-\frac{1}{2}}$ where H is the film height. MOTT[11] pointed to the difficulty that such a theory would lead to a film of very variable density. SCHIFF[12] and FRENKEL[13] suggested that the film was held on by VAN DER WAALS' forces and that such forces were great enough to permit a film several hundreds of atoms thick. On this basis, any liquid might show such films but that except in the favourable case of superfluid helium, viscosity prevented their sustenance so that the films would quickly evaporate. Such a plausible theory yields $d \propto H^{-\frac{1}{3}}$.

Two profile experiments have recently been made, one by ATKINS[14] and the other by JACKSON[15]. ATKINS used the kinetic energy of the film to make it 'overshoot' in filling a beaker and so oscillate about the bath level, rather in the manner of a liquid oscillating in a U-tube. Making some simplifying assumptions, in order to make the equations manageable, he deduced that the film thickness could be represented by $d = KH^{-n}$ where K was in the neighbourhood of 2×10^{-6} cm (varying slightly with temperature) and n was approximately 0·15, also varying somewhat with height and probably with temperature. JACKSON, viewing a static film by reflexion in polarized light found quite comparable results, so that we have a fairly complete disagreement with theory.

BIJL, MICHELS and DE BOER pointed out that irrespective of the precise theory of the film, one ought to expect the quantum relation $v \sim h/md$ to hold in the film, in other words that the film transfer velocity should vary inversely with the thickness. Since the transfer rate is very nearly if not precisely independent of height, the relation appears to apply, at any rate to a first approximation. Furthermore it agrees very nicely with earlier measurements on the flow through very narrow channels where the velocity was observed to increase as the channels diminished in width.

One additional thing can be stated fairly certainly. The heat of adsorption of helium on all solid surfaces (about 100 calories per mole) means an adsorption pressure much in excess of 25 atmospheres. Thus all surfaces in contact with liquid helium are probably covered with a layer two or three atoms deep of solid helium, and therefore the super-fluid atoms in the film can be said to skate over a thin ice of solid helium.

We must return once more to theoretical considerations. The first of the relevant theories, that due to TISZA and F. LONDON, is, as we have said before, based on the recognition that helium is a gas which obeys the BOSE-EINSTEIN statistics. In order to lose its entropy, a system which obeys such statistics goes into a condensed state at the absolute zero and the specific heat anomaly arises from the thermal energy required to lift the atoms from the ground state to the excited levels. There are difficulties here, for in the condensation of an ideal BOSE–EINSTEIN gas there is no gap between the ground and the excited levels. But to have an appreciable degree of superfluidity and to explain the magnitude of the specific heat peak in liquid helium, a relatively large energy gap is required. Futhermore, the BOSE–EINSTEIN treatment refers to a gas and not to a liquid with its strong interaction between particles. There has been a great deal of consideration of these problems and it appears to be generally agreed that there is much theoretical justification for the application of BOSE–EINSTEIN statistics to the case of liquid helium, at least in the absence of any satisfactory general kinetic theory of liquids (LONDON[16]; TISZA[17]; TEMPERLEY[18]; DINGLE[19]).

Whatever its limitations, the BOSE–EINSTEIN treatment has been extremely fruitful in the stimulation of experiments and the clarification of ideas. For example, it can be made to give a fairly satisfactory variation of ρ_n with temperature. Furthermore, it leads to an understanding of the nature of the ordered state of liquid helium at the absolute zero. Clearly one would expect no such thing as spatial order as in a crystalline solid, and experiments by TACONIS and REEKIE bear this out. The ordering must therefore take place in momentum space (phase space) which is satisfactory theoretically although more difficult to visualize pictorially.

Second Sound

Perhaps the most interesting deduction from the BOSE-EINSTEIN theory was made by TISZA in 1939. In spite of its being printed in italics in TISZA'S paper, it unfortunately passed largely unnoticed at the time, due probably to the imminence of even greater events. He noticed that if the two fluids ρ_n and ρ_s are present together, and the coupling between them is small, then it should be possible to make the two fluids oscillate in anti-phase with each other, subject to the condition of no net mass flow of liquid, i.e. $\rho_n v_n + \rho_s v_s = 0$, where v_n and v_s are the velocities of normal and superfluid respectively. The above conditions then represent a progressive wave motion in which alternate layers of liquid have an excess and a defect of entropy and are detectable as an excess and defect of temperature. They are therefore temperature waves, as TISZA called them. Such waves can be contrasted with ordinary sound waves in which the fluids move in phase and the excess or defect is one of pressure. It is interesting to note that at about the same time GANZ[20] sent a heat pulse down a long capillary of He II and estimated its velocity to be of the order of 100 metres per second. Although it was not then recognized as such, this must be considered to be the first observation of a travelling temperature wave in helium II.

In 1941 LANDAU[21] published a new theory of the hydrodynamics of a quantum liquid. This theory avoided the difficulties of the statistical treatment, and although it retained the two fluid concept of superfluid and normal liquid, it gave a new description of the energy spectrum of the liquid. Moreover, it had the additional merit of adding two new and rather pretty words to the vocabulary of physics, phonon and roton. Phonons are the DEBYE sound waves that appear in the theory of the specific heat of solids, whilst rotons, a new entity, are described by LANDAU as elementary quantized vortices. LANDAU stated that there

were two distinct energy spectra in liquid helium, a phonon
series, extending to the absolute zero, and a roton
series whose ground state is higher than the phonon ground
state, the first roton level beginning to make itself felt at
about $0.2°$ K. The theory again predicted temperature
waves, to which LANDAU gave the striking and alliterative
name of 'second sound'.

Both the theories of LANDAU and TISZA predict a value of
zero for the second sound velocity at the λ-point, and both
predict the same shape of curve down to $1°$ K with a maximum velocity of about 20 metres per second. Below that
temperature the theories diverge, TISZA predicting a zero
velocity at $0°$ K and LANDAU predicting that velocity
should rise again steeply after a shallow minimum to a
constant value of $u_1/\sqrt{3}$ at $0°$ K, where u_1 is the velocity of
first or ordinary sound.

PESHKOV[22] was the first to observe and measure the
second sound velocity down to $1°$ K, which he did by a
resonance tube method, feeding an alternating current
into a heater web at one end of a closed column of liquid
helium and, by adjusting the column length, finding the
positions of maximum response in a thermometer web at
the other end.

A race then developed to measure the velocity at lower
temperatures in order to distinguish between the two conflicting theories; a race which appears to have ended for
the time being with measurements of second sound velocity
down to $0.1°$ K by OSBORNE[23]. These show (Fig. 9) a velocity approaching a constant value of 152 ± 5 m/sec. near
the absolute zero, in fair agreement with LANDAU'S predicted value of $u_1/\sqrt{3}$ which extrapolates (from somewhat
doubtful measurements) to 155 metres per second at $0°$ K.
The agreement is also good between $0.2°$ and $0.5°$ K where
LANDAU predicts roton contributions to become effective.
The evidence is thus in favour of the LANDAU treatment
and against the concept of liquid helium as an ideal BOSE–
EINSTEIN gas. This does not mean the end of the TISZA–
LONDON theory since, obviously, helium atoms remain
BOSE–EINSTEIN particles. But it does mean that we are

G

forcibly reminded of the fact that liquid helium *is* a liquid and that we must be wary of a description in which certain atoms are labelled 'superfluid' atoms while others are 'normal' atoms in excited states. Whatever may be the true natures of the superfluid and normal fluids, their method of excitation must, as we see it at present, be described in terms of a spectrum such as LANDAU describes.

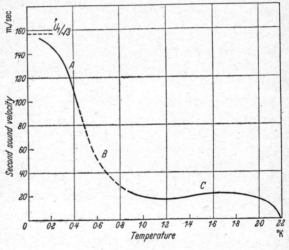

FIG. 9.

Second sound velocity in helium II.

    A: (after OSBORNE[5]).
    B: no accurate measurements exist in this region.
    C: (after PESHKOV[22], and PELLAM and SCOTT[24]).

There remain of course many puzzling things about helium. Is the frictionless transport in helium II ever as completely frictionless as the persistent current in a super-conductor which will circulate for days without observable diminution? Is the entropy of the superfluid exactly zero, and what is the nature of the interaction between super-fluid and normal fluid? For that matter, *are* there two such entities as superfluid and normal fluid?

An even greater unknown is ^{3}He. ^{3}He is odd-numbered

in the nucleus and it therefore obeys FERMI–DIRAC statistics. Electrons in a metal are also FERMI–DIRAC particles and some metals show a 'condensation' phenomenon whereby the electrons drop into the superconducting state, and this must be a quantum effect although it is not an effect predicted by FERMI–DIRAC statistics. ³He shows no sign of superfluidity down to 1° K and in a mixture with ⁴He will only go into solution in the *normal* part of He II, and not in the superfluid. Yet ³He is a quantum liquid and might therefore be expected to get rid of its entropy in some spectacular way and at a temperature well below 1° K.

In support of this idea ABRAHAM, OSBORNE and WEINSTOCK[25] have recently measured the saturated vapour pressure curve of ³He with considerable accuracy. On the assumption that the liquid state persists without change down to the absolute zero, their results show that there is nearly 0·5 entropy unit left over at the absolute zero, which would indicate that the assumption is incorrect. In other words, it is practically certain that ³He either solidifies or goes into some other kind of highly ordered state at some temperature beyond the range of the measurements, which do not at present extend below 1°K. We are thus eagerly awaiting new experiments at temperatures in the magnetic range, and in particular the specific heat curve which ought to tell us a great deal.

Once phenomena become 'understood' they lose their interest for the physicist. But on this basis, from what we have seen, interest in liquid helium will not diminish for a good many years to come.

REFERENCES

References to all papers on liquid helium published up to the end of 1939 can be found in ' Helium ' by W. H. KEESOM (Elsevier, 1942).

[1] SYDORIAK, S. G., GRILLY, E. R., & HAMMEL, E. F., Phys. Rev., **75**, 303 (1949).
[2] ANDRONIKASHVILI, E. L., J.E.T.P. (USSR), **18**, 429 (1948).
[3] BOWERS, R. & MENDELSSOHN, K., Proc. Phys. Soc., **62**, 394 (1949).
[4] KAPITZA, P. L., J. Phys. (U.S.S.R.), **4**, 181 (1941).
[5] OSBORNE, D. V., Dissertation, Ph.D. Cantab. (1950).
[6] KAPITZA, P. L., J. Phys. (USSR), **5**, 59 (1941).
[7] MELLINK, J. H., Physica, **13**, 180 (1947).

[8] ANDRONIKASHVILI, E. L., J. Phys. (USSR), **10**, 210 (1946).
[9] DAUNT, J. G. & MENDELSSOHN, K., Nature, **157**, 839 (1946).
[10] BIJL, A., DE BOER, J., & MICHELS, A., Physica, **9**, 655 (1941).
[11] MOTT, N. F., Phil. Mag., **40**, 61 (1949).
[12] SCHIFF, L. I., Phys. Rev., **59**, 838 (1941).
[13] FRENKEL, J., J. Phys. (USSR), **2**, 365 (1940).
[14] ATKINS, K. R., P.R.S., A, **203**, 119 (1950).
[15] JACKSON, L. C., & BURGE, E. J., Nature, **164**, 660 (1949).
[16] LONDON, F., J. Chem. Phys., **11**, 203 (1943).
[17] TISZA, L., Phys. Rev., **72**, 838 (1947).
[18] TEMPERLEY, H. N. V., P.R.S., A., **199**, 361 (1949).
[19] DINGLE, R. B., Phil. Mag., **40**, 573 (1949).
[20] GANZ, E., Proc. Cam. Phil. Soc., **36**, 127 (1940).
[21] LANDAU, L., J. Phys. (USSR), **5**, 71 (1941).
      ibid., **8**, 1 (1944).
      ibid., **11**, 91 (1947).
[22] PESHKOV, Phys. Soc. Conference on Low Temperature Physics (1946).
    PESHKOV, J. Phys. (USSR), **18**, 951 (1948).
[23] ATKINS, K. R. & OSBORNE, D. V., Phil. Mag., **41**, 1078 (1950).
[24] PELLAM, J. R. & SCOTT, R. B., Phys. Rev., **76**, 869 (1949).
[25] ABRAHAM, B. M., OSBORNE, D. W., & WEINSTOCK, B., Phys. Rev., **80**, 366 (1950).

SUPERCONDUCTIVITY

by K. MENDELSSOHN

Introduction

PERHAPS the most significant fact concerning superconductivity is that, although it was discovered forty years ago, we have as yet no really satisfactory explanation for the phenomenon. This is not due to a lack of experimental data or to a want of effort. In fact there is hardly another field of physics which has claimed the attention of theoretical physicists with equal frequency. Oddly enough, the steadily increasing amount of experimental evidence does not seem to have made the problem easier. On the contrary, the stage has now been reached where any satisfactory theory of superconductivity will have to account for a great number of seemingly unconnected phenomena.

One of the first researches undertaken by KAMERLINGH ONNES after the successful liquefaction of helium in 1908 was an investigation of electrical conductivity. At that time the choice seemed to lie between the gradual disappearance of electrical resistance as absolute zero is approached and a rise of resistivity to infinitely high values. Experiments carried out on mercury in 1911 showed that at helium temperatures its resistance had fallen so low that it could not be measured conveniently by the ordinary methods. Only when the sensitivity of the measuring arrangement had been improved did the great surprise become apparent that instead of gradually disappearing the resistance of the sample *suddenly* fell from a finite value to an unmeasurably small one. The temperature at which this occurs ($4 \cdot 1^{\circ}$ K) is called the transition point (T_c). How small the resistance in the superconductive state really is, we do not know. A current induced in a closed ring of superconductive metal will go on running for hours and days without measurable decrease in intensity as long as the metal is kept cold. Using such a persistent current and the most sensitive methods

95

of detection, it has now been established that the electrical resistance is smaller than 10^{-20} ohm cm, which means that for all practical as well as theoretical purposes it is *zero*.

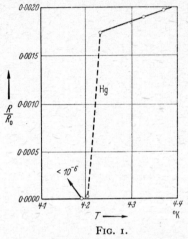

FIG. 1.

KAMERLINGH ONNES' original observation of superconductivity in mercury (1911). R = resistance of specimen; R_0 = resistance at $0°$ C. The temperature scale used at the time was incorrect, the transition occurs actually at $4 \cdot 1°$ K.

Superconductive Metals

Since the time of this first discovery all elements which can be obtained in the metallic state have been investigated at low temperatures and quite a number of them have been found to be superconductors. At first it seemed as if the occurrence of superconductivity was quite haphazard but as more metals were tested and as the measuring temperature was pushed down below $1°$ K a more regular pattern emerged. A glance at the periodic table shows that the superconductors fall roughly into two groups* and it is remarkable that all the metals concerned have more than one valency electron. Looking at a plot of the atomic volumes we see that the superconductors are contained roughly in a zone of intermediate volumes between the

---

* Recently[1] superconductivity has been reported in osmium and ruthenium, which shows that the grouping is not so strict as was once believed.

biggest and the smallest. The two distinct groups in the periodic table appear in this diagram as the elements of the falling and those on the rising parts of the volume curve. One also knows that it is the electron structure of the crystal lattice and not the nature of the atom itself which determines superconductivity. For instance, white tin which is tetragonal is superconductive but grey tin which has a cubic structure is not. Convincing evidence of the influence

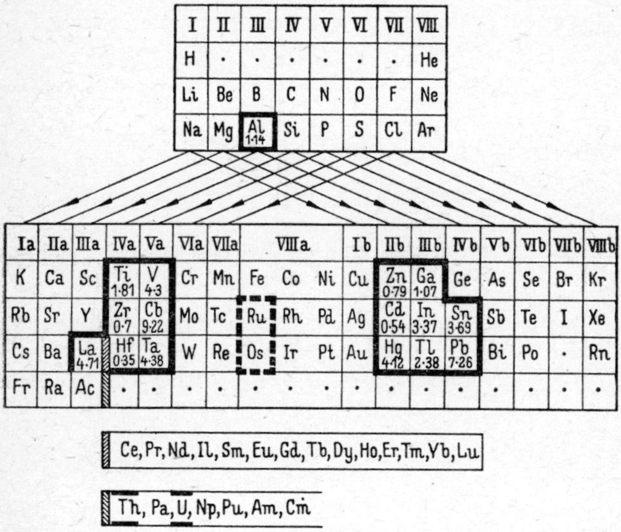

FIG. 2.
Position of the superconductive metals in the periodic table of elements.

of lattice structure is also provided by the behaviour of some alloys or intermetallic compounds. Looking at the diagram we see that neither bismuth nor gold become superconductive, as the bismuth atom appears to be some-what too big and the gold atom a little too small. On the other hand, an alloy of gold with bismuth, or more exactly the compound Au_2Bi is a superconductor. However, here the regularity ceases. If we try now to correlate the position in the periodic table, or what comes to the same in the volume diagram, with the transition temperatures of the

various metals we are not successful. The transition points
for pure metals range between 0·35° K for hafnium to 9·2° K
for columbium and they are dotted all over the map. Such
empirical attempts as have been made to discover some
rule for the transition temperatures had to fall back on less
easily determined parameters, as for instance the effective
number of free electrons in the metal, and have thereby
lost much of their value.

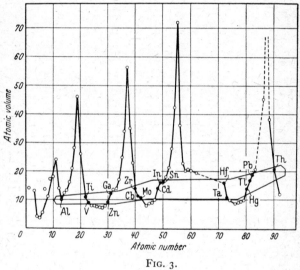

FIG. 3.
Superconductivity and atomic volume.

The question which has often been asked and which has
again come to the foreground in recent theoretical discus-
sion, is whether or not at sufficiently low temperatures *all*
metals will become superconductive. As absolute zero cannot be reached the question must clearly remain undecided
as long as any normal metals are left. However, it is apparent
that the evidence is very much in favour of superconductivity being confined to certain classes of metals or rather
to lattices with particular electron structure and density.
Another much discussed question is whether superconductivity is necessarily confined to low temperatures.

A few years ago considerable excitement was caused by a report that sodium-ammonia solutions exhibited super-conductivity at the temperature of liquid air. Subsequent experiments, however, completely failed to substantiate the claim and it seems at present that a transition point of about 14° K for the compound CbN defines the upper limit of superconductivity.

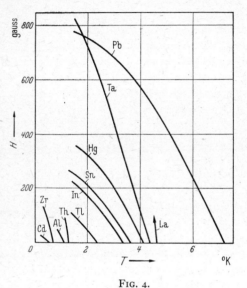

FIG. 4.
Threshold curves of superconductors.

Magnetic Effects

It was established early in the investigations that super-conductivity can be destroyed either by the application of a magnetic field or by exceeding a critical current passing through the conductor. SILSBEE suggested that these two phenomena were really one and the same and that in the case of the current perturbation the magnetic field caused by the current flowing through the surface of the wire was just equal to the external field which was known to suppress superconductivity. Thus normal conductivity can be restored in a superconductor at any temperature below the transition point by applying to it a high enough magnetic field. The field necessary to do this, the so-called 'threshold' field (H_o), varies with temperature. It is zero at the transition point, rising gradually to a temperature independent value as the absolute zero is approached. These 'threshold curves' have been measured with considerable care for most superconductors and it can be seen that they are all roughly similar in shape, being in first approximation parabolae with the centre at the absolute zero. The curves have not all the same steepness, so that besides the transition point another parameter, the value of the threshold field at absolute zero (H_o), is needed for description. Again there are roughly two groups of threshold curves, corresponding to the rising and falling path of the volume curve, the latter being a good deal steeper than the former.

A current established in a superconductor has to flow in its surface because it follows from ordinary electrodynamics that a magnetic field cannot penetrate a body of infinite conductivity. Thus if a superconductor is cooled in zero magnetic field to well below the transition point and then at a constant temperature a field smaller than the threshold value is established, this field cannot penetrate into the superconductor. This is simply due to the induction of shielding currents on the surface of the perfectly conducting metal. The latter therefore behaves in this case like a completely diamagnetic body with the susceptibility $-\dfrac{1}{4\pi}$.

We should obtain a quite different result, however, if we perform the same experiment in another way. If we establish the field above the transition point, the lines of force will penetrate the body and then according to ordinary electrodynamics no change in the field distribution should occur when the conductor is cooled in a steady magnetic field. Although its electrical resistance falls to zero, its magnetic susceptibility should remain normal. Owing to a somewhat misleading early experiment with a hollow lead sphere, this type of behaviour was in fact believed to occur, and it was only in 1933 that MEISSNER demonstrated the contrary. He showed that a solid superconductor which was cooled in such a steady field would *expel* the magnetic flux on passing the threshold curve. Consequently whichever way we perform the experiments, we are left at the low temperature with a perfectly diamagnetic body. This is an extremely important fact because now we have added to our first definition of a superconductor, that of zero resistance, a second one, that of zero magnetic induction.

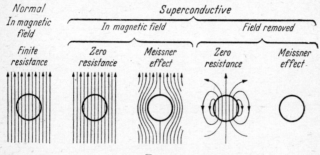

FIG. 5.

Magnetic behaviour of a sphere on cooling, showing the difference between zero resistance and MEISSNER effect.

Superconductive Electrodynamics

It is unfortunately impossible to establish a causal connection between these two conditions by means of MAXWELL'S equations, and we are forced to use both assumptions, that of zero resistance and that of zero induction, separately if we wish to account for the two fundamental experiments just mentioned. This gap in the phenomenological description was bridged by F. and H. LONDON who proposed to substitute for the ordinary acceleration equation in the case of a superconductor a new electrodynamic equation.

$$H = - \wedge c \text{ curl } i \qquad (1)$$

Acceptance of this equation which connects in an unique way the current and the magnetic field thus leads to the postulate that two types of conduction are possible in a metal, firstly ordinary conductivity which follows

MAXWELL'S equation and secondly superconductivity which
requires for its description this new connection not contained in ordinary electrodynamics. The new equation satis-
fies a number of important conditions. It accounts for zero
resistance as well as for the change to zero induction on
passing the threshold curve. It also clears up an awkward
difficulty arising out of the behaviour of multiply connected
conductors. The postulate of zero induction is sufficient to
explain what will happen in a sphere or an ellipsoid when
it is cooled to superconductivity. In the superconductive
state and with the surrounding field the surface of the
sphere will carry a current of exactly the size and distribution to account for its complete diamagnetism. When the
field is reduced to zero the current, too, disappears. However, if instead of a sphere we would have cooled a ring in
a steady field the fact that the material of the ring has
become perfectly diamagnetic does not mean that the lines
of force threading the hole have been expelled. If now in
the superconductive state the external field is reduced to
zero, the magnetic flux through the ring will remain trapped
and we are faced with a persistent current. No such current
would exist in the ring if it had been cooled to the same
temperature in zero magnetic field. We see here that the
condition of zero induction is insufficient while on the other
hand the behaviour of the ring follows rigorously from the
LONDON equation.

Since superconductivity is a strange phenomenon which
only occurs in the neighbourhood of absolute zero, we are
inclined to regard its peculiar electrodynamic behaviour,
too, as odd and irregular. However, there is a beautiful
symmetry and simplicity in the connection between magnetic field and current which is completely missing in
ordinary conduction. In the latter case we have a steady
current causing a steady magnetic field but not vice versa.
In the superconductor, on the other hand, a steady magnetic
field will also cause a steady current. If FARADAY had
experimented with superconductors as well as with normal
ones, he would probably have considered the latter as pre-
senting the more difficult problem.

The Penetration Depth

The origin of the new electrodynamics which incidentally has since been fully worked out and extended particularly by v. LAUE, is of some interest. It occurred independently to BECKER, HELLER, SAUTER and to H. LONDON that the magnetic field must penetrate a little even into a super-conductor because the charge is not a homogeneous fluid. By accounting for the charge and the inertia of the electrons, these authors showed that on the surface of the conductor the current and with it the field must enter to a finite depth which was estimated to be about 10^{-5} cm. This penetration depth which denotes the distance at which the magnetic field on the mathematical surface on the conductors has dropped to the eth part is intimately connected with the constant Λ in the LONDON equation. Its experimental measurement has led to a great number of different investi-gations. The constant Λ determines penetration depth δ directly as

$$\delta = c \sqrt{\frac{\Lambda}{4\pi}} \tag{2}$$

As we shall see presently, there is a close relation between the threshold value of the magnetic field and the difference of the free energies in the superconductive and the normal state. This is based on the fact that the magnetic induction in the superconductive material is zero. Since the depth of penetration of the field into the superconductor is very small, this condition is generally fulfilled because the thin skin δ in which the induction differs from zero represents usually only a very small fraction of the superconductive volume. However, if we extend our experiments to pro-gressively thinner slices of superconductive material this skin effect must become more noticeable and can provide a means for determining δ. For thermodynamic reasons we can expect that the threshold value of a superconductor of linear dimensions comparable with the penetration depth should be *raised* and this effect has actually been found by measurements on thin wires and evaporated metal films.

In the case of the former calculation has indeed shown the value of 10^{-5} cm to be correct. Experiments have also been made on the magnetic induction of colloidal superconductive particles as well as by very careful measurements on the bulk metal. The latter ones give clearly the most direct evidence of δ, but unfortunately they do not lead to absolute values, yielding only the variation of δ with temperature. As was expected, it was found that δ decreases first rapidly below the transition point, gradually approaching a constant value at $T \doteq 0$. It follows from electrodynamical theory that

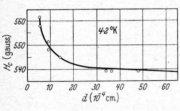

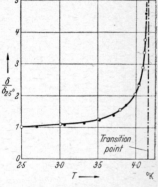

FIG. 6.

Variation of the magnetic threshold field H_c of lead with the diameter d of the superconductive wire. The points are experimental values obtained by PONTIUS and the curve the function calculated by VON LAUE.

FIG. 7.

Variation with temperature of the penetration depth δ in mercury. The circles are values derived from resistance measurements on thin films by APPLEYARD et al. The points are derived from induction measurements on colloids by SHOENBERG. The values are normalized at $2.5°$ K.

this decrease is closely linked with the effective number of superconductive electrons.

There is also another way of attacking the problem. A light wave being an electromagnetic vibration should of course be reflected without dissipation from a metal having infinite conductivity. However, experiments have shown that in the infra-red the optical absorption of the metal is the *same* in the superconductive and in the normal state. This result can be understood on the basis of the detailed theories mentioned above, because the electron inertia will make itself felt. Since the charge does not move in a mathematical layer on a surface the light wave will act on the normal as well as on the superconductive electrons in the metal and in contradistinction to a D.C. measurement *both* conduction processes the normal as well as the superconductive one will come into play. This has indeed been demonstrated by experiments with high frequency currents. As the wave lengths of the applied radio frequency is shortened, energy dissipation in the metal begins to make its appearance. Looking at the problem in quite a different way we can correlate the transition temperature to a critical frequency by the fundamental equation

$$k \ T_c \sim h \ \nu_o \qquad (3)$$

Recent experiments are beginning to approach this critical frequency ν_o which corresponds to a wavelength of rather less than 1 cm and it will be interesting to see whether as this frequency is passed dissipation will occur even at temperatures very near to the absolute zero. These experiments, too, allow an evaluation of the penetration depth which again in order of magnitude agrees well with the measurements of conduction and susceptibility.

It is interesting to note that into these considerations has crept the concept of a two-fluid model, somewhat similar to the one used so profitably in the case of liquid helium. The two separate conduction processes which form the basis of the LONDON electrodynamics strongly suggest the existence of two interpenetrating electron fluids, one normal and the other superconductive, whose relative concentration varies with temperature. It is, however, well to remember that one cannot, of course, differentiate between electrons except by assigning relative numbers of them to different energy states and while the model is an extremely useful one, its application is only justified as long as its limitations are kept in mind. Provided this caution is observed one may talk of 'superconductive' and 'normal' electrons which allow an easy method of distinction between the energy states and their population.

Superconductive Alloys

The first indication that superconductive regions of small geometrical size may behave differently as regards their threshold value from the bulk metal, was obtained in a rather roundabout way from observations on superconductive alloys. These alloys often have very much higher threshold values than any of the pure metals which at first sight seems to lead to rather extraordinary consequences. As already mentioned, the threshold values are directly related to the free energy of the metal and the values of H_c on alloys suggested free energies of such a magnitude as would be difficult to account for. A large number of investigations on the induction and thermal energy of these alloys showed that they behave rather differently from pure metals. For instance, they will not expel the magnetic flux on cooling through the threshold curve and when the alloy is in the superconductive state the lines of force will remain 'frozen in'. Moreover, calorimetric measurements have demonstrated that the energy content of superconductive alloys is not very different from that of a pure metal. From these results it was concluded that a superconductive alloy is a magnetically inhomogeneous structure; a 'magnetic sponge' whose skeleton is made up of small regions of exceedingly high threshold value. Rough as this model is, it seems to account quite well for the various phenomena exhibited by superconductive alloys.

Superconductive Thermodynamics

Leaving aside the problems presented by superconductors of small size and magnetically inhomogeneous structure, we are justified in treating a lump of pure superconductive metal as a volume of space from which, on passing through the threshold curve magnetic flux is ejected. This process is, of course, tantamount to doing work against the MAX-WELL tensions in the same way as work is done by the piston in a cylinder against the pressure of a gas. This immediately gives the magnetic threshold value the significance of an equilibrium curve in a diagram of state.

difference (
which will
conductive.
proportiona
region of
whole of th
when the
mean, of cc

where γ is
This hypot
independer
the entrop
indeed equ
mation. In
vide a muc
investigatic
obscured b
it would b
FELD speci
easily be
metals. A
tion metals
value of γ
the positiv
actually fo
threshold (
conductive
positive hc
conductive
We have
at the trai
order. Wr
latent heat
terms of th

According

The two areas separated by it denote the normal and the superconductive states which are 'phases' in the true thermodynamical sense. We can now determine the differences in thermodynamic quantities by using the threshold value as the only significant parameter.

If F_s is the free energy of the superconductive metal in zero magnetic field, its free energy in a field has a value $F_s - \frac{1}{2}HI$ where I represents magnetization of the specimen. Since the superconductor is perfectly diamagnetic $I = \frac{-H}{4\pi}$. At the threshold curve, where $H = H_c$, we therefore obtain between F_s and the free energy in the normal state (F_n) the following equation:

$$F_n = F_s + \frac{H_c^2}{8\pi}$$

or for the difference in free energy between the two states for one mol of the substance:

$$F_n - F_s = \frac{H_c^2}{8\pi} V \qquad (4)$$

where V is the atomic volume.

Since the entropy S is directly related to the free energy by:

$$S = -\frac{dF}{dT}$$

we obtain for the difference of entropy between the two states:

$$S_n - S_s = -\frac{H_c}{4\pi} \frac{dH_c}{dT} V \qquad (5)$$

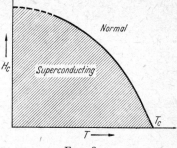

FIG. 8.

The threshold curve separates the superconductive from the normal region in the thermodynamic diagram of state.

H

the transition from the superconductive into the normal
state takes place and vice versa, except at the transition
point ($H_c = 0$) and at the absolute zero ($T = 0$).

Thus the superconductive and the normal regions in our
diagram of state correspond to two phases which are
separated in space and which in transformation into each
other will develop a latent heat. The first observation of this
latent heat was carried out adiabatically in order to demon-
strate the existence of a magneto-caloric effect which can
have either positive or negative value. The possibility of

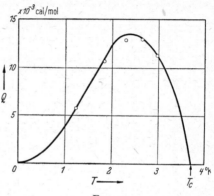

FIG. 10.

The latent heat required to transform one mol of tin from the superconductive into the normal state. The curve has been calculated from formula
(7) and the points are direct measurements by KEESOM and VAN LAER.

using these effects to obtain low temperatures has already
been discussed by Dr. KURTI in his lecture. Since then
isothermal determination of the latent heat have also been
carried out. The difference in specific heat between two
phases is directly connected with the difference in entropy
by

$$\Delta C = T\, \frac{d\Delta S}{dT}$$

One thus obtains for the difference between the superconductive and the normal state

$$C_s - C_n = \frac{T}{4\pi} \left\{ H_c\, \frac{d^2 H_c}{dT^2} + \left(\frac{d H_c}{dT} \right)^2 \right\} V \qquad (8)$$

As can be seen, the specific heat of the metal in the normal state is higher than in the superconductive state near absolute zero. Then at a temperature corresponding to the maximum value of $(S_n - S_s)$ the relation is reversed. At the

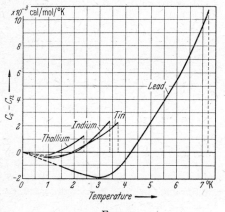

FIG. 11.

Differences in the electronic specific heat C_s–C_n for some metals obtained from the threshold curves by formula (8). (DAUNT, HORSEMAN and MENDELS-SOHN.)

transition point, where H_c becomes zero, the first term of the equation disappears and we get

$$(C_s - C_n)_{T_c} = \frac{T_c}{4\pi} \left(\frac{dH_c}{dT}\right)^2_{T = T_c} V \qquad (9)$$

This shows us that thermally the transition point is distinguished by the lack of a latent heat and by a discontinuity in the specific heat. This discontinuity is related directly to the steepness of the threshold curve, a relation which has indeed been well substantiated by experiments. A number of interesting relations emerge under the simplifying assumption that the threshold curve is strictly a parabola. The electronic specific heat in the superconductive state will then be proportional to the cube of the temperature and the discontinuity at the transition point will be 2 γ T_c.

Whether or not the electron specific heat in the superconductive state follows exactly a T^3 function, it is clear from the entropy differences that at sufficiently low temperature, the superconductive electron entropy becomes negligibly small in comparison with the normal one. The

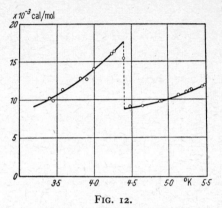

FIG. 12.

The discontinuity in the specific heat at the transition point of tantalum. (DÉSIRANT and MENDELSSOHN.)

good agreement between $(S_n - S_s)_{T \to 0}$ and γT in fact allows us to conclude that near absolute zero *all* the electrons normally contributing to the thermal energy of the electron gas have passed into the superconductive state.

Superconductivity and Order

For the understanding of the curious problem presented by superconductivity, the entropy function gives an important clue. Plotting the electronic entropy of the metal in the superconductive and in the normal state, we see that over the whole range of temperatures from absolute zero to the transition point the superconductive state is the one of lower entropy that means of a higher degree of order than the normal state. Leaving aside for a moment the question what can be the pattern of this order, we must first find out what other manifestations there are of this ordered state. The non-resistive flow of charge clearly appears to be connected with this new type of order. Since, as is evident from the threshold curve, the charge which can be transported through the superconductor without dissipation decreases with rising temperature, it seems tempting to link up the phenomenon of zero resistance with the gradual approach of the superconductive entropy to the normal one as the transition point is approached. Using the concept of the two-fluid model, one would then suspect that the rise in entropy of the superconductive metal as it is warmed up must be due to the lifting of super-conductive electrons into a higher energy state. Once they are in this higher state, the electrons evidently have lost the ability to participate in the super-current. Thus, as one

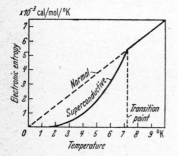

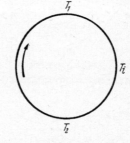

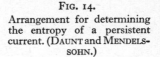

FIG. 13.	FIG. 14.
The electronic entropy of lead in the superconductive and normal states.	Arrangement for determining the entropy of a persistent current. (DAUNT and MENDELS-SOHN.)

would expect, the high degree of order in the supercon-ductor and the phenomenon of the super-current appear to be closely connected and the question arises as to the entropy transported by such a current.

At first sight it may seem that this is a question which cannot be answered since it is normally impossible to measure the entropy of a certain energy state within the substance. However, in the case of the superconductor this is feasible because the electrons in these states obey different electrodynamic equations. Dealing, for instance, with a direct current below threshold strength, the entropy carried will only be that of the super-current. The experiment itself is simple. If we determine the temperature in the middle of a wire whose ends are kept at constant but different temperatures, our measurement will be influenced by the fact whether or not a current passes through this wire. If the electron fluid in the wire is in motion it should influence the temperature distribution along its length in the same way as a flow of water will influence the temperature distribution along a tube connecting two reservoirs of different temperature. In both cases we deal in effect with a determination of the specific heat. This reversible thermal effect of a wire carrying a current in a temperature gradient is, of course, well known; it is the THOMSON heat. Normally the determination of the THOMSON coefficient in a metal is somewhat difficult because it is small and masked by the irreversible JOULE heat. However, in the case of a superconductor these difficulties disappear. Taking a ring of, say, lead wire which is kept at different temperatures T_1 and T_2 at opposite ends of a diameter, we have only to measure the intermediate temperature T_i somewhere along the ring. The temperature is again measured after inducing in the ring a persistent current which can be very strong (at $4°$ K about 100 amps in a wire of 1.5 mm diameter). The super-current does not cause irreversible heating and thereby allows a very accurate determination of the THOMSON coefficient. The actual determination has shown that the THOMSON coefficient in lead is at least 500 times smaller in the superconductive state than in the normal state. So to all intents and purposes the entropy carried by the super-current is *zero*. This is indeed a most remarkable result. It tells us that even at finite temperatures, the assembly of superconductive electrons is in a state of complete order; it is energetically at absolute zero. This result does not, of course, entail any infringement of the third law of thermo-dynamics because the superconductive electrons are 'dissolved' in a fluid of normal ones so that at any finite temperature the whole assembly will have finite entropy.

It thus appears that, as a metal is cooled below the transition point, an ever increasing proportion of the free electrons pass into the state of zero entropy. This state is not a phase in the ordinary sense because it is not separated in position space from the rest of the substance. Nevertheless, we continually carry out experiments in which only this state is concerned, as for instance in the induction of a persistent current. The realization that the phenomenon of superconductivity is intimately connected with a state of complete order of part of the electron system is of great importance in its interpretation. However, before we turn to a field which up till now is largely speculation something must be said about the remaining phenomena.

The Intermediate State

In our consideration of the work done against the MAXWELL tensions when a superconductor is brought through the threshold curve, we have tacitly assumed that the demagnetization factor of the specimen is zero, i.e. that we deal with an infinitely long needle in a longitudinal magnetic field. While this ideal state can be approached in some experiments, it cannot be realized in others as, for instance, in measurements of the specific heat on a lump of superconductive metal. The distortion of a field by a sample with magnetic permeability different from 1 is, of course, a general feature of all magnetic measurements. However, whereas normally the susceptibilities of substances are small enough to make this distortion merely a correction factor, the complete diamagnetism of a superconductor will produce distortions of the same absolute magnitude as the applied magnetic field. Let us consider for instance the case of a sphere in a gradually rising homogeneous external field. Denoting the undistorted field, i.e. the field in sufficient distance from the disturbing superconductor, as H, then we find that the field on the magnetic equator of this sphere will be $3/2H$. This means that when the external field has reached a value of $2/3 \, H_c$ the threshold value H_c obtains at the equator of the sphere. Any further increase of the external field must now result in a destruction of superconductivity in part of the metal; and here we are faced with a curious dilemma. One might think at first sight that the sphere would be reduced gradually to a superconductive ellipsoid surrounded by the rest of the metal in the normal state, and that this ellipsoid would get more cigar-shaped as the external field is increased. This, however, is not permissible as will readily be seen from the following argument. Let us assume a thin tube of magnetic flux is entering the sphere at its equator, then the magnetic tension on that side of our tube which faces the interior of the sphere will always be greater than on the outside. In other words such a bent tube of flux enclosed in a homogeneous magnetic medium cannot exist and it must straighten out. As it turns out, the only possible solution would be the splitting up of the whole sphere into

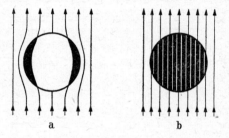

FIG. 15.

The co-existence of the superconductive (white) and the normal (black) phase at the transition of a sphere. The state (a) is impossible since it offers no homogeneous solution. The metal must split up into an inter-mediate state (b), made up of superconductive and normal threads or laminae.

straight superconductive and normal threads which lie in the direction of the external field. A rigorous solution of the problem is, however, by no means simple. The question arises what, for instance, would be the thickness of these threads in order to give the energetically most favourable distribution. Such solutions as have been put forward rely on a number of assumptions. The depth δ to which the field can penetrate a superconductor which we have mentioned before must play an important part and so does any surface tension which may exist between the two states. A very awkward situation arises in the region inside the metal where the threads are piercing the geometrical surface of the superconductor. The solution requires that here the original threads separate into finer and finer ones so as to ensure homogeneous conditions on the surface.

That such an 'intermediate' state does in fact exist cannot be doubted. Plotting the measured equatorial field of a superconductive sphere against the external field it is indeed observed that at first it rises proportional to 3/2 of the value of the external field. When the external field has become $2/3\ H_c$, the value H_c has been reached at the equator and the picture changes abruptly. The equatorial field now remains *constant* as the external field is increased which means that the sphere is beginning to be penetrated by the magnetic flux. Finally, when the external field has reached the threshold value, equatorial and external field have become equal and from now on remain equal; the sphere has completely passed into the normal state. These peculiar magnetic conditions have a number of

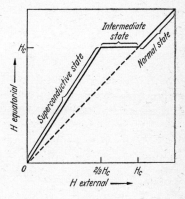

FIG. 16.

Variation of the equatorial magnetic field of a sphere with the external magnetizing field (measured at infinite distance from the specimen) on changing from the superconductive to the normal state.

important consequences for the actual measurement of the various quantities concerned. For instance, determinations of the threshold value have to rely either on a close approach to the ideal condition of a needle in a longitudinal field or have to be taken from the values at which the induction undergoes a sudden change (at $2/3\ H_c$ and H_c) in a sphere or an ellipsoid. Equally it is impossible to obtain an isothermal latent heat unless the ideal condition of the longitudinal case is fulfilled. The actually determined latent heats are therefore spread out over a range of temperatures due to

the demagnetization factor of the specimen on which they
have been obtained.

Measurements of the magnetic field in the narrow equatorial gap of a sphere have indeed revealed indications of
the thread-like structure of the intermediate state, although
it seems at present that the size of the individual threads
is very much larger than might be expected from theory.
Even so, one gains the impression that a sphere or an
ellipsoid, once the superconductive surface has been
broken, will be in a tolerably homogeneous magnetic state
which is truly intermediate between the superconductive
and the normal one.

Transition Phenomena

The position gets much more difficult, however, when we
consider a body of less regular shape. For instance, a *short*
cylinder with its axis in the direction of the field will not
admit to a homogeneous solution and it seems certain that
besides domains which may possibly split up in the same
manner as in the sphere, there will exist purely superconductive and purely normal regions. In this case we
would therefore meet a true phase boundary between the
superconductive and the normal metal. This state of affairs
is probably responsible for a strange phenomenon which
has been observed in magnetic as well as calorimetric
measurements. It is found very often that after a *sudden*
change of field or temperature the magnetic induction or
the thermal energy will change *gradually*, sometimes taking
as much as five minutes to reach a new value. In the
transition region where superconductive and normal
material are co-existent, a change in one of the variables of
state will cause a redistribution of the two phases, neces-
sitating the displacement of a phase boundary. This
boundary is the surface, inside the metal, which carries a
current, and its shifting depends on the time needed for
the current to adjust itself to the new equilibrium conditions. Since at these low temperatures the resistivity even
of the normal metal is very small, the re-adjustment of
current path and strength is a slow process. From what has

been said before it is clear that one would expect such big shifts of a phase boundary to be more likely in an irregular body and this can be demonstrated by a direct experiment. If the induction of a short cylinder is measured it will show these time effects in a very pronounced manner. However, when the same cylinder is shaped down to a sphere, the induction measurement shows no such relaxation.

This question of currents dying out slowly in a very highly conducting boundary surface whose resistance on the other hand is certainly different from zero, raises the problem of the sharpness of the transition. KAMERLINGH

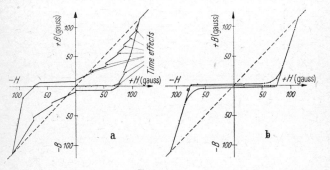

FIG. 17.

(a) Variation of the magnetic induction B in a short cylinder of tin with the external magnetic field H, showing the occurrence of time effects. When the same cylinder is shaped into a sphere, the magnetic cycle (b) shows no time effects. (MENDELSSOHN and PONTIUS.)

ONNES' early observations had already shown the abruptness with which the resistance disappears and subsequent experiments have emphasized this feature. As the sample of metal investigated is made progressively more and more pure chemically as well as physically the temperature interval over which the transition takes place gets smaller. For a very pure single crystal and extrapolating to zero measuring current the change appears to be a truly discontinuous (within less than 10^{-3} degrees). At any other temperature than at the transition point the question becomes much more complicated. To effect such a transition of the resistance we have to apply a magnetic field and the distortion of the field caused by the specimen has to be considered. Until recently it was generally believed, however, that even in a magnetic field the resistance change would be discontinuous and that such broadening as has been observed might be due to distortion of the field or to the effect of impurities. Recent careful measurements have cast a certain amount of doubt on this conception of a discontinuous transition, because in all cases even for very pure metal wires perfectly aligned in the magnetic field, a finite width of the transition was found which tended to

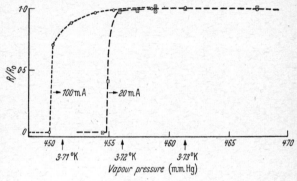

FIG. 18.

As the measuring current is reduced, the temperature interval over which the resistance transition to superconductivity takes place becomes progressively smaller. (MACDONALD and MENDELSSOHN.)

zero as the transition point is approached.[2] Abrupt transitions in an external field, however, have been observed in cases where a specimen definitely distorted the field and these seemed to be closely connected with a peculiar resistance hysteresis which has been known for a long time.

Gradual change of resistivity does not, of course, as yet infringe our concept of two separate phases because the latter is based on the change of induction and not of resistance. The inductive change indeed seems to be abrupt but one has to remember that because of the demagnetization factor of the specimen employed the decision is not as clear cut as one might wish. Moreover, there exist other effects which further complicate the interpretation of the observed data. It is sometimes found that as a lump of metal is cooled in a magnetic field, superconductivity only sets in at a rather lower temperature than is indicated by the threshold curve. The phenomenon is similar to the supercooling of a vapour below the saturation value. Evidently, an extra energy is required in order to form a superconductive 'drop' in the normal metal, just as it is needed to form a drop of liquid. The possible existence of such a surface tension at the interface between normal and superconductive metal has already been mentioned when we discussed the formation of laminae in the intermediate state. Evidence for it is also provided by the complete expulsion of the magnetic field from, say, a long cylinder in a longitudinal field, on becoming superconductive. Indeed, it is difficult to see why the metal should not prefer instead to split up into a large number of small superconductive and normal needles if it were not for the fact that the formation of the large inter-face requires too much energy. Such needles, orientated in the direction of the external field and small in diameter compared with the depth of penetration, would permit superconductivity without decreasing appreciably the value of the magnetic field inside the metal. It is interesting to note that such behaviour does in fact occur in superconductive alloys where the inhomogeneities of structure are evidently big enough to overcome the surface tension. So far the experiments cannot give more than a very rough estimate of the surface energy, nor is it known whether the energy is the same when the boundary of the superconductive state coincides with the geometrical surface of the metal. Here is clearly a large field where only further experiments can give a definite answer.

Another insufficiently explored set of phenomena are the thermo-electric ones. For a long time a search has been made to find a feature which would betray a superconductor above the transition point. There are, as I mentioned, a number of rough indications regarding the position in the periodic table of elements, but on the whole there is no

physical property known which foreshadows superconductivity. The only exception may be possibly found in the
behaviour of the thermo-electric force. There exist no
thermo e.m.f. between superconductors, but there seems
to be some indication that slightly above the transition
point the thermo-electric properties of superconductors
may begin to deviate in a characteristic manner. Here again
it has to be left to further work to make a decision.

Heat Conductivity

There is also still a large measure of uncertainty in our

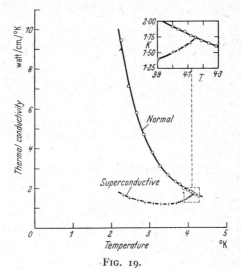

FIG. 19.

Thermal conductivity of pure mercury in the superconductive and in the
normal state. (HULM.)

knowledge of the heat transport in superconductors. Since
it is a good deal more difficult to measure the thermal
resistance than the electric resistivity of a metal, rather less
data are available on the former. The heat conduction of a
metal is largely due to its free electrons and an interesting
change in this quantity might be expected when the
electrical conduction becomes infinite. Early experiments
did, however, yield no conclusive results beyond the fact

that the thermal resistance does *not* become zero at the transition point. More recent work has in fact shown that the heat flow in the superconductive state is not larger but a good deal *smaller* than in the normal state. While this was not the kind of result one would have predicted, it can be readily explained when one remembers that the superconductivity electrons, having zero entropy, cannot contribute to the heat flow.

In all cases investigated so far, the heat conduction in the normal state seems to be a smooth function of the temperature. This means that below the transition point the values of the heat conduction in fields higher than H_c represent a continuation of the curve above this temperature. The curve for the superconductive metal begins to deviate from this function at the transition point and the ratio of superconductive to normal heat conduction decreases steadily as the temperature is lowered. Unfortunately this ratio is not the same function of temperature for the different metals and the phenomenon is clearly one of considerable complexity. There is no discontinuity in the heat conductivity at the transition point but while in some metals the superconductive and normal curves deviate gradually at this temperature, they depart abruptly in others.[3]

The problem is made still more difficult by the behaviour of some alloys and pure metals under strain.[4] In these, too, the curve for the normal metal is the continuous one from which the superconductive heat conduction departs at the transition point. Now the deviation is, however, in the opposite sense, the superconductive metal conducting heat better than the normal phase. Making up specimens with graded admixtures of a second component, this change in behaviour from a pure metal to an alloy has been traced step by step.[5] There exists no intermediate stage in concentration for which the heat conduction is always the same in the superconductive and the normal state. Instead, the two curves intersect at some temperature below the transition point, showing that we are faced with two competing processes whose dependence on temperature is different. One of these is the gradual passage of electrons into the state of zero entropy but about the other we are still very much in the dark. Possibly it is due to an enhanced lattice conduction or perhaps an entirely new form of heat transport may make its appearance. This could, for instance, be a circulation process involving superconductive and normal electrons similar to the return flow of normal and super-

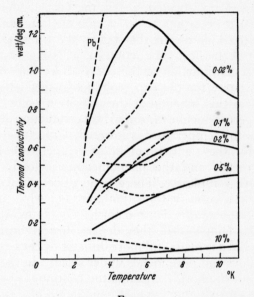

FIG. 20.

Thermal conductivity of lead with different percentages of bismuth in the superconductive and in the normal state.
——————— Normal
– – – – Superconductive
(MENDELSSOHN and OLSEN.)

fluid liquid in helium II. Here, too, more experimental evidence is required before the question can be settled and what has come to light recently does not appear to make the problem simpler. The anomalous behaviour is only shown by some alloys while others exhibit a heat conduction similar to that of a pure metal. Furthermore, it has been found that in some specimens the heat conduction during the transition in a magnetic field is lower than either in the normal or in the superconductive state.

Practical Application

The question is often asked, and quite naturally, whether the extraordinary electrodynamic properties of a super-conductor may not lead to important practical applications. First it has to be remembered here that in spite of the great advances made in cryogenic technique the production and maintenance of very low temperatures is still a formid-able problem as a practical proposition. The use of super-conductors in electrical machinery is also greatly limited because of the relatively small magnetic energy which such equipment can handle. All available information on threshold values indicates that a maximum value of 1,000 gauss at absolute zero is the best that can be obtained. This is of course a very small field to be tolerated as maximum. From what we have said concerning super-conductive alloys it is clear that their very high threshold values up to 10,000 gauss or more do not correspond to an equally high magnetic energy. There is in fact only one application of superconductivity which has seriously been suggested and it has also been tried. That is the use of a superconductor as a sensitive bolometer. The low heat capacity and the almost limitless steepness of the resistance-temperature curve form an ideal device for the detection of weak signals. The development of such an instrument has been helped by the discovery of superconductivity in columbium nitrite with a transition temperature ($\sim 14^\circ$ K) which can be obtained by the use of liquid hydrogen. The conditions are therefore somewhat simplified since no liquid helium is required.

As was already mentioned, there seems little reason to expect superconductivity at substantially higher tempera-tures. A small ray of hope is given by the observation that strain may under certain circumstances raise the transition point of a metal considerably. However, no experiment has yet been made which by this means extends the range of

I*

superconductivity beyond that already obtainable with columbium nitrite.

Finally the question has cropped up occasionally whether the phenomenon of superconductivity may not be due to spin orientation, with infinite conductivity as a somewhat secondary consequence. That such a model cannot be true at least in the crude sense is shown by the determination of the gyro-magnetic effect. This has yielded a LANDÉ g-factor of 1 which means that the diamagnetism of superconductors is produced by ordinary electron currents and is not due to electron spin.

Theory

I began this lecture by saying that as yet we have no satisfactory explanation of superconductivity and while this statement seems to do little justice to the efforts of theoretical physicists, those who have worked in the field will have sympathy with it. There have been too many hopes and too many disappointments. There has of course been success as you have seen in the thermodynamic and above all in the electrodynamic treatment. But these interpretations are essentially phenomenological ones. Whatever indications they give as to the actual mechanism of superconductivity, these definitely remain vague hints. Such attempts, on the other hand, as have been made on the basis of a definite microscopic model have not met with equal success. Even so, as the years have gone by, the theoretical picture has been narrowed down appreciably. It now seems clear that in order to explain superconductivity, the microscopic model will have to fulfil a number of conditions. First of all, it is necessary to find an interaction mechanism leading to an electronic energy state in the metal which corresponds to the small excitation energy kT_c. Secondly, one would expect this state to be separated from the continuum of states by an energy gap to account for the type of specific heat function observed. Finally, and most important of all, it will have to be shown that this energy state will give rise to the strange electromagnetic phenomena by which superconductivity is characterized. The fact that the new state corresponds to an energy of only 10^{-4} electron volts makes it clear that it cannot be ascribed to such things as the direct action of the Coulomb force. Regarding the nature of the electron interaction leading to superconductivity, two recent theories, those of HEISENBERG and of BORN and CHENG as well as the ideas of F. LONDON favour Coulomb exchange interaction as the operative agent in the creation of the superconductive state. HEISENBERG'S theory first proposed the existence of an electron lattice. These ideas have often been expressed in the past, but it can be shown that in an electron lattice with the same constant as that of the ionic lattice the high potential barrier prevents the shift of these lattices through each other. HEISENBERG'S lattice was one of a much larger lattice constant. More important than the condensation in position space appears to be the condensation in momentum space on the surface of the Fermi sphere, but here again one runs into considerable difficulties. The model would require that at absolute zero the sphere is completely covered with the electron 'condensate' and as the temperature is raised this would gradually evaporate. The theory further requires that this evaporation should be asymmetrical, leaving a hole at one place on the surface of the momentum sphere. Such a state of affairs means that in the lowest energy state spontaneous currents must exist in a superconductor. These currents may compensate each other and that would be the reason why they are not observable but there are other serious objections against the lowest energy state carrying a current. It is also implicit in the theory that at sufficiently low temperatures *all* metals (except the ferromagnetic ones) should become superconductive. As mentioned above, this does not seem to be particularly likely in view of the observed facts. The work of BORN and CHENG is interesting because of an empirical rule which they have found between lattice structure and the occurrence of superconductivity. They found that such metals are superconductors in which the FERMI sphere practically coincides with the corners of a BRILLOUIN zone. Superconductivity is therefore interpreted as the redistribution of electrons from the corners of the zone to the top of the FERMI surface. However, this theory, too, postulates the existence of currents in the lowest energy state.

The state of flux in our ideas concerning the mechanism leading to superconductivity is perhaps best demonstrated by the fact that these ideas have again completely changed since this lecture was given. While for some time it was taken for granted that superconductivity had its origin in some electron-electron interaction and that the crystal lattice simply fulfilled the function of a temperature independent container, FRÖHLICH[6] has quite recently postulated a very different interaction mechanism. FRÖHLICH considers (and similar ideas have been put forward independently by BARDEEN[7]) the interaction of the electrons with the lattice vibrations. Starting from BLOCH's theory of electronic conductivity he finds that through the influence of the PAULI principle the interaction energy between the electrons and the vibrational field will depend on their distribution in momentum space. A strong enough interaction of this type can lead to a ground state which differs from the FERMI distribution. This ground state will, however, only be realized if the interaction between lattice vibrations and electrons exceeds a certain value. Assuming this state to be responsible for superconductivity, the energy must depend on the mass M of the atoms in the vibrating lattice. Consequently, the transition temperature T_c must be mass dependent and the postulated relation has the form $T_c \propto M^{-\frac{1}{2}}$.

Subsequent measurements of the transition temperatures of the isotopes of mercury,[8] tin,[9] and lead[10] have in fact shown a variation with the mass. The effect is small but the results leave no doubt that it exists and that it is roughly of the predicted form. The anticipation by the theory of this effect is the more remarkable because earlier experiments had indicated its non-existence.

There can be little doubt now that superconductivity is due to an interaction of the lattice vibrations with the electrons. Further, the experiment must be regarded as strong evidence for the mechanism postulated by FRÖHLICH and also that the latter is the reason for the appearance of the superconductive state. Unfortunately, mathematical difficulties have so far made it impossible to show that under the influence of this interaction the ground state will exhibit the phenomena of superconductivity. Even with this limitation, the advance which has been made by the new theory is considerable. The prediction and discovery of the isotope effect have narrowed down very much the choice of mechanisms which can be held responsible for the appearance of superconductivity.

Conclusion

The formidable mathematical difficulties which any microscopic theory encounters when trying to explain the phenomena of superconductivity is strangely out of keeping with the simple symmetry of the electrodynamic equations. One cannot help feeling that what is missing is not only a microscopic theory of superconductivity but a new concept in physics. It must be admitted that the theoretical interpretation of a state which requires a solution of the quantum mechanical many body problem presents tremendous difficulties. On the other hand, fundamental concepts in physics have so far been found to be simple. This rule of simplicity is of course only an empirical one and we have no other reason than our experience to assume that our brain should be particularly fitted to comprehend as simple the fundamental mechanisms of natural phenomena.

Here we enter the field of pure speculation where observed facts can act as a guide but where it would be foolish to believe that we are still sure of conclusive reasoning. The best we can do is to try to formulate the problem, to try to comprehend this new thing which has to be explained. Speculation is notoriously dangerous, but there is no progress without speculation. We are within our rights as long as we admit this danger and do not try to look upon our speculation as established facts.

It seems to me that the new physical facts which have to be explained are not so much concerned with the particular model of superconductivity but rather with a new form in which the particles of matter can associate. There is a curious analogy between the two unexplained low temperature phenomena, that of superfluidity in liquid helium and that of superconductivity. In both cases we find that at a certain temperature the degree of order in the system suddenly increases. In both cases this increase of order is coupled with the appearance of a transport of mass or charge which is free of friction. In both cases the rate of this transport is temperature dependent. It starts from zero and rises gradually to a constant value as the absolute zero is approached. Once this critical rate is exceeded, the ordinary semi-classical transport mechanism reappears.

It would indeed be rash to conclude from this analogy that the cause of the two phenomena is the same. In fact the most likely explanation for the phenomena in helium, that this is a condensation of a non-ideal BOSE-EINSTEIN gas (which is now supported also by the observations on ^3He) would not be applicable to the free electrons which obey FERMI-DIRAC statistics. On the other hand this fact may possibly emphasize the fundamental character of the new state which will be exhibited by such different assemblies as helium atoms and free electrons.

Indeed, instead of pointing out how unlikely it is that helium atoms and electrons should behave in very much the same way, we should be impressed by the fact that these assemblies *in spite* of the marked differences show the same phenomena. The apparent universality of behaviour should induce us to accept it as something fundamental. The key to the understanding of the new concept in physics appears to be in our hands, it is the rapid drop of the entropy. There is no sign either in a superconductor or in liquid helium that the electrons or atoms crystallize into an ordered pattern. On the contrary, the formation of a crystal seems to be clearly prevented by the high zero point energy in both cases. However, like all our models, our conception of order is derived from our daily experiences. Since we always see order as a regular pattern of things in respect to their position in space, we are apt to forget that the description of a set of particles is not complete with the co-ordinates of space; it also requires the co-ordinates of momenta. Except for the limitations of our visual imagination, there is no reason why order should be established only according to positions and not equally well according to velocities. We have no right to assume that the order in a fluid must be less than in a crystal because the particles making up the fluid are not arranged in a chessboard pattern. In fact the electron fluid in a metal, just as liquid helium must be at absolute zero in as much a state of perfect order as, let us say, the crystal lattice of a diamond. Here perhaps we find the reason for the analogy between superconductivity and liquid helium. The forces holding together a crystal lattice may be very different in different crystals. They may be ionic forces, VAN DER WAALS' forces or exchange forces. The result however is always the same: a regular pattern in space. It is equally possible that the mechanisms responsible for superconductivity and for superfluidity in helium may be quite different but they seem to lead to the same thing: a regular pattern in velocities. If this speculation would turn out to be true, and as yet we see no reasons against it and many reasons for it, the low temperature phenomena will have revealed to us a fourth state of aggregation of matter. This fourth state of aggregation, an ordering or condensation with respect to the momenta, should then take its rightful place as equal among the three states of aggregation of positional order.

REFERENCES

Reference to individual papers is only made in the case of those which have appeared in the last two years. An almost complete list of references up to 1949 can be found in the following books and articles:

STEINER, K., and GRASSMANN, P.; 'Supraleitung', Vieweg, Brunswick 1937.
SHOENBERG, D.; 'Superconductivity', Cambridge University Press 1938.
JACKSON, L. C.; Reports on Progress in Physics, Vol. 6, London 1939.
MENDELSSOHN, K.; Reports on Progress in Physics, Vol. 10, London 1946.
MENDELSSOHN, K.; Reports on Progress in Physics, Vol. 12, London 1949.

[1] GOODMAN, B. B.; Nature, 167, 111 (1951).
[2] MACDONALD, D. K. C., and MENDELSSOHN, K.; Proc. Roy. Soc. A 200, 66 (1949).
[3] HULM, J. K.; Proc. Roy. Soc. A 204, 98 (1950).

[4] MENDELSSOHN, K., and OLSEN, J. L.; Proc. Phys. Soc. A 63, 2 (1951).
[5] MENDELSSOHN, K., and OLSEN, J. L.; Proc. Phys. Soc. A 63, 1182 (1951);
     Phys. Rev. 80, 859 (1950).
[6] FRÖHLICH, H.; Phys. Rev. 79, 845 (1950); Proc. Phys. Soc. A 63, 778
     (1950).
[7] BARDEEN, J.; Phys. Rev. 79, 167 (1950).
[8] MAXWELL, E.; Phys. Rev. 78, 477, 1950; SERIN, B., REYNOLDS, C. A.,
     and NESBITT, L. B.; Phys. Rev. 78, 487 and 813; 80, 761 (1950).
[9] MAXWELL, E.; Phys. Rev. 79, 173, 1950; ALLEN, W. D., DAWTON, R. H.,
     LOCK, J. M., PIPPARD, A. B., SHOENBERG, D., BÄR, M., MENDELSSOHN,
     K., and OLSEN, J. L.; Nature, 166, 1071 (1950).
[10] OLSEN-BÄR M.; Nature, 168, 245 (1951).

For accounts of the electrodynamic theory see:

VON LAUE, M.; 'Theorie der Supraleitung', Springer (1947).
LONDON, H.; 'Macroscopic Theory of Superconductivity', Wiley (1950).